D1572098

WHITE DWARFS–BLACK HOLES

ACADEMIC PRESS RAPID MANUSCRIPT REPRODUCTION

WHITE DWARFS–BLACK HOLES

An Introduction
to Relativistic Astrophysics

by

Roman Sexl
Hannelore Sexl
Institute for Theoretical Physics
University of Vienna
Vienna, Austria

Translated from the German by
Patrick P. Weidhaas
Lawrence Livermore Laboratory
Livermore, California

ACADEMIC PRESS
A Subsidiary of Harcourt Brace Jovanovich, Publishers
New York London Toronto Sydney San Francisco
1979

6323-9723 ✓

PHYSICS

ACADEMIC PRESS, INC.
111 Fifth Avenue, New York, New York 10003

United Kingdom Edition published by
ACADEMIC PRESS, INC. (LONDON) LTD.
24/28 Oval Road, London NW1 7DX

Library of Congress Cataloging in Publication Data

Sexl, Roman Ulrich.
    White dwarfs—black holes: An introduction to
    relativistic astrophysics.

    Translation of Weisse Zwerge, schwarze Löcher.
    Includes index.
    1.   Astrophysics.   2.   General relativity
(Physics)   3.   Black holes (Astronomy)
4.   Cosmology.   I.   Sexl, Hannelore, joint author.
II.   Title.
QB461.S3913   523.01   79-23307
ISBN 0-12-637350-7

Originally published under the title of
WEISSE ZWERGE - SCHWARZE LOCHER
© Rowohlt Taschenbuch Verlag, GmbH,
Reinbek bei Hamburg, 1975.
All Rights Reserved

PRINTED IN THE UNITED STATES OF AMERICA

79 80 81 82   9 8 7 6 5 4 3 2 1

CONTENTS

PREFACE

Since the discovery of quasars, pulsars, black holes, and the cosmic background radiation, general relativity theory and relativistic astrophysics have become focal points of current physical and astronomical research. Additionally, the tremendous advancements of experimental technology have led to a vast amount of new results, all confirming and strengthening the predictions of Einstein's theory—predictions that only a decade ago were hardly verifiable by experiment. For anyone who is not an expert in astrophysics, it is almost impossible to gain sufficient information on all these exciting new discoveries. Reading the scientific literature requires thorough knowledge of the complex mathematical techniques of general relativity. On the other hand, the majority of popular articles dealing with Einstein's theory and its applications are strictly qualitative and can only hint at the intricate ideas involved.

Our concern for the situation of the teacher provided the main motivation for writing this book: Being questioned by his or her students about new discoveries, the teacher, who is only familiar with the popular literature is frequently unable to provide in-depth information. In addition, the typical college education of a teacher, experimental physicist, astronomer, or mathematician does not include courses dealing with the fascinating world of ideas being opened up by general relativity theory, and taking place on the borders of mathematics, physics, astronomy, and epistemology. In order to rectify this situation, we began to introduce (in Austria) seminars and courses that would present the physical arguments and problems of relativistic astrophysics correctly but without any higher mathematics (i.e., mathematics beyond differential and integral calculus). The organization of these lectures was significantly inspired by Dr. Edward Szirucsek (Secretary of the Ministry), and we would like to express our deep gratitude for his support.

The reader of this book is expected to have had an introductory course in physics, as well as a good background in calculus. We might mention that only a part of the exercises in this book are meant to reinforce the mathematical formalism; the remaining exercises (e.g., Problems 3.4–3.7) try to stimulate the reader into thinking more about the ideas that are presented in the text. We should also warn the reader that the problems covered in Chapters 7 and 8 are currently the subject of much discussion and controversy. It is quite possible that in the future some of the statements in these chapters might have to be partially revised. Nevertheless, we decided to include the material in the book since otherwise the reader would not be able to follow the future development of these topics.

For years, the Foundation for the Advancement of Scientific Research has generously supported our work. Also, this book could never have been written without international contacts with other research teams; for instance, the joint seminars with Munich and Trieste. Particular thanks are due to the Austrian Academy of Sciences, which provided the Institute for Space Research with funds to hire an additional employee and enabled us to participate in the international congresses on relativity theory in New York and Tel-Aviv. The pleasant working environment during a research visit to the European Nuclear Research Center, CERN, at Geneva was also of great help in completing this book.

We would like to extend our thanks to Prof. Dr. J. Ehlers, Prof. Dr. W. Thirring, Dr. E. Streeruwitz, and Dr. H. Urbantke for reviewing the manuscripts and for their many valuable suggestions. We are also indebted to Mr. H. Prossinger and Dr. R. Beig for their assistance in producing the illustrations. The laborious task of typing the different versions of the manuscripts was handled admirably by Mrs. F. Wagner and Ms. E. Klug. Finally, we must thank all the participants of those courses and lectures during which, after many didactic experiments, we gradually conceived this book.

Vienna   **Roman and Hannelore Sexl**

PREFACE
To the Second German Edition

During the four years that have passed since publication of the first edition of this book, relativistic astrophysics has continued to rapidly advance. Improved atomic clocks are now used to detect the relativistic time dilatation in airplanes with an accuracy of up to 1%. Advances in x-ray astronomy and in other observational techniques have given us new insight in our search for black holes. Today, we suspect massive black holes in the central cores of globular clusters and active galaxies. After an initial, stormy developmental phase, the search for gravitational waves has now been put on a more solid foundation. New generations of detectors are expected to provide definite answers in the coming years. Perhaps the most significant result, at least theoretically, has been the discovery of thermal radiation being emitted by black holes! At this point in time, it is not clear, however, whether Stephen Hawking's theoretical prediction of this radiation will lead to empirically measurable consequences.

By incorporating these recent developments, we hope the second (German) edition of this book will continue to serve as an up-to-date guide through the fascinating field of relativistic astrophysics.

Roman and Hannelore Sexl

CHAPTER 1

THE FOUNDATIONS OF THE
GENERAL THEORY OF RELATIVITY

In the years 1905, 1915, and 1925, three events took place
that dramatically altered the course of modern physics. In 1905
Albert Einstein formulated the special theory of relativity, in
1915 he put forward the general theory of relativity, and in 1925
quantum mechanics assumed its final form. Since then physics has
progressed rapidly, yet no further theories of comparable impact
have been discovered.

Beginning in 1930 quantum mechanics and special relativity
were merged into relativistic quantum field theory. This unifica-
tion was quite rewarding in that it led to--at least a partial--
explanation of the laws and interactions governing elementary
particle physics, a process that even today is far from being
complete.

Four types of forces (electric, strong, weak, and gravitational) came to be known, of which the first three could be
explained through particle interactions taking place in the flat
space-time of special relativity. A mysterious exception seemed
to be the gravitational force: In order to describe gravity,
Einstein in 1915 was compelled to follow a road that led him far
beyond the ideas of his special theory of relativity, eventually
explaining the gravitational force as the geometric *curvature of
space-time*.

For a long time, Einstein's theory of the gravitational field,
the *general theory of relativity*, occupied an extremely isolated

1

position within the domain of modern physics.   This was due partly
to the mathematical framework of the theory, which is based on
abstract geometric concepts ("Riemannian geometry") that play no
significant role in the rest of physics.   In other words, the
study of general relativity requires knowledge of a rather complex
mathematical apparatus (tensor calculus), which is not needed in
other physical applications.

The extreme difficulty in devising suitable experiments that
could verify the general theory of relativity also contributed to
the isolation of that theory.   After all, Newton's theory described the gravitational field with an accuracy that was quite
sufficient for all practical purposes, while for a long time, general relativity could come up with only three classical tests for
its verification (Chapter 2).   In fact, for several decades no
further experimental verification of the relativistic theory of
gravitation appeared feasible.

Even Hubble's discovery of the *expansion of the universe* in
1929 did not change the situation significantly.   The experimental
material was much too inaccurate to contribute to the postulation
of a reasonable cosmological model of the universe.   As a result,
during the decades from 1930 through 1960 there was almost no interest in general relativity.

Finally, in about 1960, a turning point was reached: advanced
technological capabilities combined with fresh ideas opened up
previously inaccessible avenues for the experimental verification
of general relativity.   Since then, physics and astronomy have
joined forces to form the discipline now called *relativistic
astrophysics*.   This field has produced a steady stream of experimental and theoretical research into general relativity theory.
The climax of this activity is probably the physics of *black holes,*
which we shall discuss in Chapters 6 and 7.

This book is an attempt to provide insight into some older as
well as current problems and results in relativistic astrophysics.
The reader will find that such insight can be gained without

having to develop the complex mathematical machinery of general relativity. The required mathematics would be beyond the scope of this book anyway. Our approach will be to derive all results within their correct order of magnitude (i.e., up to factors of perhaps 3 or 5, which we shall simply ignore). As much as possible, our reasoning will be based on simple and well-known physical principles, requiring only a knowledge of calculus for the mathematical deductions. *The understanding of the main principles of Einstein's theory of general relativity is possible without advanced mathematics.*

THE EÖTVÖS-DICKE EXPERIMENT

In their first encounter with physics, students generally learn a basic property of the gravitational force: in a gravitational field all bodies fall equally fast (in a vacuum) or, worded differently, *inertial and gravitational mass are identical* (better yet, proportional to each other).

This assertion is by no means self-evident and must be verified experimentally. How accurately is the proportionality between inertial and gravitational mass known today? The first elementary experiments were performed by Galileo, who showed that the oscillation time of a pendulum does not depend on its material but solely on its length. During the years between 1890 and 1922, Baron Eötvös undertook a famous series of experiments to demonstrate the material independence of the gravitational attraction. In the course of those 30 years he eventually increased the precision of his experiments to such a degree that in 1922 he verified the equivalence of inertial and gravitational mass to an accuracy of 10^{-9}. Forty years later, between 1960 and 1963, Dicke and his team repeated the Eötvös experiment in Princeton. The outcome was an increase in precision to 10^{-11}.

Problem 1.1: Eötvös-Dicke Experiment

In a hypothetical experiment two balls are released at the same time from the same altitude, and continue to fall toward the earth's center. Based upon the Eötvös-Dicke experiment, to what degree of accuracy do their centers of mass maintain the same relative altitude?

INERTIAL SYSTEMS

As we have seen, the equivalence of inertial and gravitational mass has been known for a long time and is one of the most accurately measured fundamental facts of physics. Newton's theory of gravity reflected this fact correctly, and consequently for a long time no one realized how remarkable this phenomenon really was. What makes the material independence of gravity so extraordinary comes to light if one recalls the enormously intricate structure of matter: complicated atomic nuclei, consisting of protons and neutrons, are surrounded by complex electron orbits that are responsible for the multitude of chemical reactions. *Yet all materials fall with identical acceleration in a gravitational field.* Should we not suspect an inherent reason for this puzzling behavior? Should we not, in fact, design the theory of gravitation in such a way that inertial and gravitational mass are indistinguishable right from the start?

These are precisely the questions that guided Einstein to the general theory of relativity. Here the point of departure is an initial analysis of the consequences that follow from the Eötvös-Dicke experiment. These consequences have been demonstrated most impressively in the television broadcasts from the spaceships that have circled the earth or have been on course to and from the moon. When a spaceship falls freely in the gravitational field of earth, moon, or any other celestial body, a state of weightlessness will prevail inside. Since all objects inside the spaceship are subjected to the same gravitational acceleration as the ship, it is impossible to detect the existence of any gravitational field in its interior.

In fact, all bodies inside the ship follow Newton's first law *(law of inertia)* since their motion is straight and uniform (i.e., unaccelerated). Now any system (like our spaceship) that has the property that in the absence of exterior forces objects will move unaccelerated is called an *inertial system*.

The fundamental idea of general relativity can now be formulated as follows:

> *In a gravitational field free-falling reference systems*
> *are inertial systems.*

A glance at Fig. 1.1, however, reveals that this statement can only be valid in sufficiently small space-time regions. In Fig. 1.1a, we see three objects (dots), which float freely (and unaccelerated) in a tiny spaceship orbiting earth. In contrast, Fig. 1.1b demonstrates how objects that are located below the center of mass of a large spaceship will slowly accelerate toward earth while objects above the center of mass will drift away from earth. The huge spaceship therefore does not constitute an inertial system.

In Fig. 1.2 Newton's concept of the gravitational field is contrasted with Einstein's. It is apparent from Fig. 1.2 that the

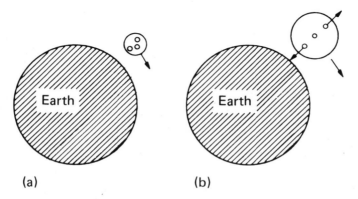

(a)   (b)

Fig. 1.1. Spaceships and inertial systems.

Newton

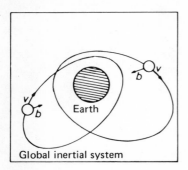

Global inertial system

Einstein

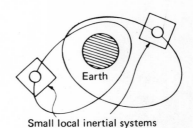

Small local inertial systems

A large global inertial system does exist. The gravitational forces inside it are determined by the mass distribution (earth). A force acts on falling objects.

Free–falling reference systems are small local inertial systems. The mass distribution (earth) determines the relationship among these inertial systems. No forces act on freely falling objects.

Fig. 1.2.   Newton's vs. Einstein's concept of the gravitational field.

mutual relationships among the small inertial systems is governed by the mass distribution, and that, in general, their relationships are quite complicated. Contrary to Newton's theory (and also to the special theory of relativity) the many small local inertial systems cannot be combined to one large global inertial system.

A simple-minded but relevant geometric model may explain the situation further. In Fig. 1.3 we show a portion of a warped surface. Every sufficiently small surface element can be approximated by the (Euclidean) geometry of a plane. All these small flat surfaces, however, will resist any attempt to assemble them into a large plane. Instead, they bear some complicated relationship to each other, this relationship being determined by the curvature of the surface. The surface curvature in our model corresponds

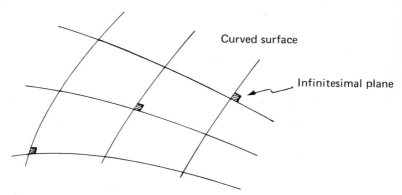

Fig. 1.3. Locally a warped surface is approximated by the geometry of a plane. The relationship among these infinitesimal planes is governed by the curvature of the surface.

precisely to the influence of the mass distribution in general relativity, while each of the tiny flat surface elements corresponds to a local inertial system. In Chapter 3, we shall return to this analogy when we discuss the space-time concept of general relativity.

THE EQUIVALENCE PRINCIPLE

Systems that fall freely in a gravitational field are locally inertial systems. This is the conclusion of the previous section, which we want to illustrate here from a slightly different angle.

Now Fig. 1.4 depicts two laboratories of which one rests on the earth's surface while the second one falls freely toward earth. The freely falling lab constitutes an inertial system. The lab on the earth's surface is accelerated (upward) when viewed from this inertial system. But a system that is accelerated with respect to an inertial system cannot itself be an inertial system, but must be an accelerated system. Consequently, the physical phenomena observed inside the lab on the ground should be identical to those observed in a laboratory that is also accelerated but this time with the help of a rocket in outer space. Our reflections can be summarized in the *equivalence principle*:

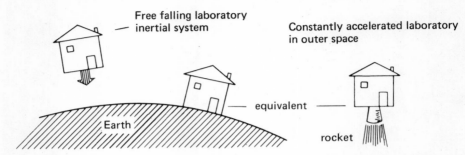

Fig. 1.4. A laboratory resting on the earth's surface is accelerated with respect to a freely falling inertial system. All physical phenomena will be identical to those inside a laboratory that is constantly accelerated by a rocket.

Physical phenomena in accelerated systems and gravitational fields are equivalent. No experiment conducted inside a laboratory can distinguish whether this lab exists in a gravity field or whether it is being accelerated due to some external force (e.g., a rocket).

By adopting this principle the agreement of inertial and gravitational mass becomes trivial. Inertial mass is by definition the resistance of an object against acceleration. But the gravitational field is caused precisely by the acceleration against the freely falling reference system.

To conclude: in Einstein's theory inertial and gravitational mass are, in principle, indistinguishable.

Problem 1.2:   Inertial and Gravitational Mass

Suppose someone discovers a molecule with different inertial and gravitational mass. How can this be checked? What would be the consequences for Newton's and Einstein's gravitational theories?

THE GENERAL THEORY OF RELATIVITY

Building upon the equivalence principle and the analogy (Fig. 1.3) with curved surfaces, Einstein, after nearly ten years of work, was able to formulate a complete theory of the gravitational field, the general theory of relativity.

His main concern was finding the *field equations* that permit the determination of the gravitational field (i.e., the mutual relationships among the local inertial systems), given the mass distribution.

The predictions of general relativity theory are for the most part in agreement (at least as far as the solar system is concerned) with those of Newton's theory. Only in a few instances do we come across relativistic correction terms that are concerned with the behavior of light and of moving bodies in a gravitational field. These new effects comprise the famous tests of general relativity and will be covered in Chapter 2.

The field equations of general relativity do not follow uniquely from the equivalence principle. They are rather the simplest equations consistent with the basic ideas presented above. In the decades since the formulation of Einstein's theory, a number of rival theories of gravity have been proposed (the best-known being the *scalar-tensor theory or Dicke-Brans theory* whose basic concept is due to Pascual Jordan). All of these theories, however, are based on Einstein's fundamental idea, namely, the equivalence principle. They differ in that they postulate different and more complicated relationships between mass distribution and gravitational field.

In the following discussion of the experimental tests of general relativity we shall in each instance distinguish whether the measurements only test the physical foundation of the theory, i.e., the equivalence principle, or whether they also throw light on the particular relationship between mass distribution and gravitational field that is predicted by the field equations.

CHAPTER 2

THE CLASSICAL TESTS OF GENERAL RELATIVITY

This chapter is devoted to a discussion of the three "classi-cal" tests of the general theory of relativity. Using Newton's theory as a guide we shall derive all three relativistic effects only within their correct order of magnitude, without insisting on exact numerical factors. After all, a derivation of the correct factors would require application of the complete set of field equations as well as the involved space-time concept of general relativity.

THE RED SHIFT

The most well-known effect predicted by the general theory of relativity concerns the red shift of light rays under the influ-ence of a gravitational field (in particular the earth's field). This effect is also the easiest to calculate. Let us consider a light ray rising against a gravitational field. If ν is the light's frequency, then each photon will have an energy $E = h\nu$, h being Planck's constant. Associated with this energy is a photon mass

$$m = \frac{E}{c^2} = \frac{h\nu}{c^2} \tag{2.1}$$

Of course, m is not a rest mass since the photon's rest mass is clearly zero!

While climbing, the photon has to do work against the field:

$$W = m \, \Delta U \tag{2.2}$$

10

where ΔU is the gravitational potential difference between start
and endpoint of the light path.

As a result, the photon will arrive at the top with reduced
energy

$$E' = E - W \tag{2.3}$$

Associated with E' is a reduced frequency ν', which is obtained
from (2.2) and (2.3):

$$\nu' = \nu \left(1 - \frac{\Delta U}{c^2}\right) \tag{2.4}$$

Expressing the red shift as the frequency difference $\Delta\nu = \nu - \nu'$,
we conclude:

red shift: $$\frac{\Delta\nu}{\nu} = \frac{\Delta U}{c^2} \tag{2.5}$$

In 1911 Einstein for the first time theoretically predicted
this shift in frequencies. Since then, it has been experimentally
tested many times by measuring the red shift of spectral lines of
the light emitted from the sun and from very dense stars (white
dwarfs). Now the gravitational potential (according to Newton) at
the surface of a star with radius R is

$$U(R) = GM/R \tag{2.6}$$

while at the point of observation (earth, being far away) $U \approx 0$.
Consequently, $\Delta U = GM/R$, so Eq.(2.5) yields

$$\Delta\nu/\nu = GM/Rc^2 \tag{2.7}$$

Since the left-hand side of (2.7) is dimensionless this must
be true for the right-hand side. The expression

$$R = 2GM/c^2 \tag{2.8}$$

therefore has the dimension of a length. R is called the
Schwarzschild radius of the mass M, and plays a central role in
general relativity. In terms of the Schwarzschild radius we can

express the red shift (2.7) of starlight by the simple formula

$$\Delta\nu/\nu = \mathcal{R}/2R \qquad (2.9)$$

This equation demonstrates the important fact that the red shift is directly proportional to the ratio of the Schwarzschild radius to object radius. We shall see that this ratio also determines all the other relativistic effects. In other words, knowledge of the ratio $\mathcal{R}/R$ is crucial for estimating relativistic phenomena.

In Table 2.1 we have listed the masses, radii, Schwarzschild radii, and the ratios $\mathcal{R}/R$ for a variety of objects in our universe $(2G/c^2 = 1.5 \times 10^{-27} \text{ mkg}^{-1})$.

A glance at Table 2.1 shows that for a white dwarf star we should expect a red shift $\Delta\nu/\nu \approx 10^{-4}$, an effect that should be easily measurable. Unfortunately, it turned out to be a rather difficult experimental problem. The main difficulty was trying to separate the gravitational red shift effect from the Doppler-shift effect caused by the star's initially unknown motion.

Precise measurements of the gravitational red shift only became feasible in 1965 when Pound and Snider succeeded in measuring the red shift of spectral lines in the earth's gravitational field. Utilizing the Mössbauer effect, they measured a relative frequency shift $\Delta\nu/\nu = 2.5 \times 10^{-15}$ over a distance of only 20 m!

TABLE 2.1

Object	Mass (kg)	Radius (m)	$\mathcal{R}$ (m)	$\mathcal{R}/R$
Atomic nucleus	10^{-26}	10^{-15}	10^{-53}	10^{-38}
Atom	10^{-26}	10^{-10}	10^{-53}	10^{-43}
Human being	10^{2}	1	10^{-25}	10^{-25}
Earth	6×10^{24}	6×10^{6}	9×10^{-3}	10^{-9}
White dwarf	2×10^{30}	10^{7}	3×10^{3}	3×10^{-4}
Neutron star	2×10^{30}	10^{4}	3×10^{3}	$0,3$
Sun	2×10^{30}	7×10^{8}	3×10^{3}	10^{-6}
Galaxy	10^{41}	10^{21}	10^{14}	10^{-7}

This shift is so minute that for visible light the frequency would be reduced by only 1 Hz. The Pound-Snider experiment has been performed repeatedly since 1965, resulting in an increase of accuracy to within 1%. The gravitational red shift has therefore been established as one of the most accurate tests in support of general relativity.

Unfortunately, the red shift also happens to be the weakest support for general relativity. In fact, Eq.(2.5) follows (almost) exactly[1] from energy conservation, i.e., without involving general relativity. Moreover, the quantum-mechanical assumptions were used only in order to simplify the derivation, and could have been avoided. This becomes apparent by looking at Eq.(2.5), which does not contain Planck's quantum-mechanical constant h.

Problem 2.1: Pound-Snider Experiment

Compute the red shift for light that rises in the earth's gravitational field (which can be considered to be homogeneous). Verify the magnitude of the red shift in the Pound-Snider experiment. What is the role of the Mössbauer effect in red shift measurements?

THE DEFLECTION OF LIGHT

Light traveling through the gravitational field of a mass will be curved under the influence of that field: we already know that even light is subjected to gravity. While moving through the gravity field of a star (say, the sun) the light is being deflected from a straight course by an angle δ, as shown in Fig. 2.1.

The deflection of light can be discussed almost as easily as the red shift of spectral lines due to gravity. The difference is

---

[1] *Equation (2.5) is exact for $R/R \ll 1$ since it constitutes the first term in an expansion of R/R. The general formula for arbitrary values of R/R is presented in Chapter 6.*

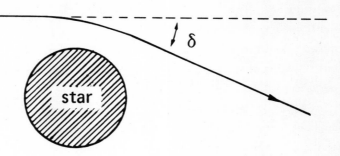

Fig. 2.1. Path of a light ray traveling through a star's gravitational field.

that our elementary derivation will not suffice to derive exact results. We shall only approximate the correct order of magnitude as well as the nature of the effect. This fact is an indication that the gravitational light deflection is a true test of general relativity in the sense that it cannot be predicted accurately without making full use of that theory. As a matter of fact, Einstein himself committed a well-known error by attempting to calculate the deflection without using his full theory. The answer that he gave in 1911 turned out to be too small by a factor of 2. He had made use of Newton's theory, which, however, is only applicable to speeds that are small compared to the speed of light.

We are going to compute the deflection of light traveling through the sun's gravitational field. In Fig. 2.2 we depict the simple approximation that we shall use.

On its path through the field, the maximal deflection of the light beam takes place closest to the sun. Here the gravitational acceleration can be approximated by

$$g \approx MG/R^2$$

which rigorously holds only at the sun's surface. Our assumption will be that this acceleration is in effect for an interval of approximately $2R$, i.e., the solar diameter, while outside this

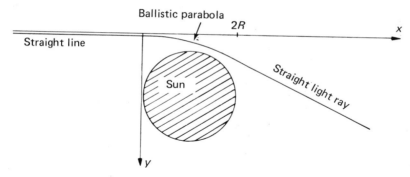

Fig. 2.2. Calculation of the light deflection.

interval the light follows a straight line (see Fig. 2.2). Thus, the beam forms a ballistic parabola, given by

$$y = \frac{g}{2}t^2, \qquad x = ct \tag{2.10}$$

Here we have set $x = ct$ since the velocity component in the y direction is negligibly small. Looking at Fig. 2.2, we see that the deflection angle δ is given by the slope of $y(x)$ at $x = 2R$:

$$y(x) = \frac{g}{2c^2}x^2 = \frac{GM}{2R^2c^2}x^2$$

$$y'(x) = \frac{GM}{R^2c^2}x \tag{2.11}$$

$$\delta = y'(2R) = \frac{2GM}{Rc^2}$$

Our answer is

$$\delta_N = \frac{2GM}{Rc^2} = \frac{R}{R} \tag{2.12}$$

Again, the ratio of Schwarzschild radius to (solar) radius determines the magnitude of the effect. The index N is a reminder that we have calculated the Newtonian value for the light deflection. It was obtained for the first time by Söldner in 1801, and coincides with the result derived by Einstein in 1911. Our simplistic

approach has yielded the same answer since we (a) over-estimated
the gravitational acceleration, but at the same time (b) under-
estimated the distance of gravitational influence to be only as
long as the solar diameter.   Both these errors happen to cancel
each other, thereby resulting in our correct (Newtonian) answer.

In contrast, the answer provided by general relativity calls
for a light deflection that differs by a factor of 2 from that
given in Eq.(2.12).   Thus,

$$\text{light deflection: } \delta = \delta_E = \frac{2R}{R} \tag{2.13}$$

Up until several years ago the gravitational deflection of
light remained a fairly unreliable test for general relativity.
This is seen by contrasting Einstein's theoretical prediction
against the experimental results: for a light beam that just
grazes the sun's surface, Einstein's formula (2.13) predicts a
deflection of

$$\delta_E = \frac{2 \times 3 \text{ km}}{7 \times 10^5 \text{ km}} = 8.57 \times 10^{-6} = 1.75'' \tag{2.14}$$

where we have used $R_\odot = 7 \times 10^5$ km for the solar radius.   On the
other hand, observations that were made during various solar
eclipses resulted in values ranging from 1.5" to 2.2".[2]

Figure 2.3 shows some typical observational results that were
obtained during the eclipse of 1922 by Campbell and Trumper.   That
figure is a superposition of two photographs.   First, the stars in
the sun's vicinity are photographed during a total solar eclipse.
Later, the same field of stars is again photographed at night.
The effect of the light deflection reveals itself as an outward
shift of the stars during the eclipse (see Fig. 2.4).   These
shifts are indicated by line segments in Fig. 2.3.   Note that

―――――――――

[2]*Positions of stars close to the sun can only be measured
during a solar eclipse.*

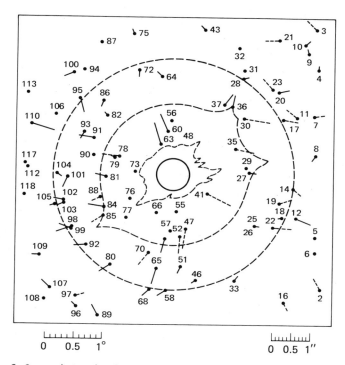

Fig. 2.3. Historical measurements of the light deflection (1922).

these shifts were drawn highly magnified (compare the two scales), for otherwise they would not appear visible to the naked eye.

Figure 2.5 summarizes the analysis of the data gained during the historical observations of 1922 and 1929. According to that figure, the predictions made by the general theory of relativity (dotted line; $\delta = 1.75''$ for $R = R_\odot$) are compatible with the observational data, although their mean values (dash-dotted curve) approach a value of $\delta \approx 2.3''$ at the sun's surface.

In the decades following 1930 only minor improvements were made in the measurements of the gravitational deflection of light. Beginning in 1969, however, much progress was made through radio-astronomic methods. Annually, on 8 October the quasar 3C279 is obscured by the sun, and the deflection of the radiowaves emitted

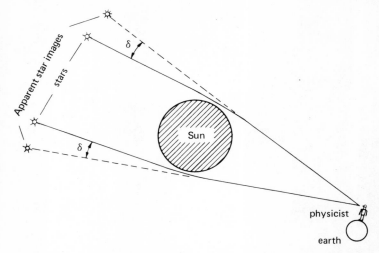

Fig. 2.4. Effect of the light deflection on the apparent positions of stars.

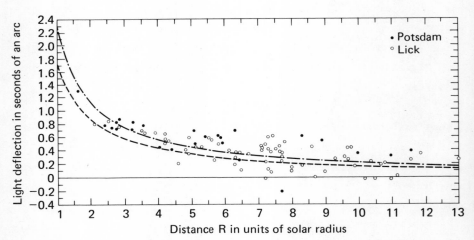

Fig. 2.5. Light deflection as a function of the distance from the sun (historical data from 1922 and 1929).

by that object can be measured shortly before and after that event.

Measurements conducted over the past few years resulted in a mean value of

$$\delta = 1.73" \pm 0.05" \tag{2.15}$$

This result verifies Einstein's predicted value for the light deflection [Eq.(2.13)] to an accuracy of approximately 3%.

In Chapter 3 we shall discuss another experiment that deals with the behavior of electromagnetic waves in a gravitational field. This recent experiment--the Shapiro experiment--is also in agreement with general relativity to within a few percent.

Problem 2.2: What Is Straight?

Since even light rays are curved in a gravitational field, the question arises how to define "straightness." Discuss this question with your colleagues and record the answer(s). We shall return to this problem later. For now the question is only intended to stimulate your imagination and to demonstrate that a problem exists.

THE PERIHELION SHIFT

So far, our discussions centered around the motion of light under the influence of gravity. The immense success of Newton's theory, however, is due to its description of the movement of masses, in particular the planets, in a gravitational field. Since Newton's theory describes this motion quite accurately, we can expect any relativistic predictions to involve only a very small correction to Newton's classical results.

This correction term is the shift of the perihelion. Here is a brief explanation of this effect: according to Kepler's *second law* the orbits of the planets are ellipses, the sun occupying one of the two foci. The point of the orbit that is closest to the sun is called the *perihelion*. According to Kepler, the perihelion

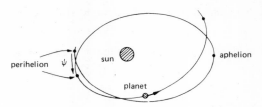

Fig. 2.6. The shift of the perihelion.

is a *fixed point* on a planet's orbit. General relativity revises Kepler's second law by predicting a rosette-shaped orbit (see Fig. 2.6). Thus, the perihelion is not fixed, but gradually rotates around the sun.

This effect has two causes, which can be understood heuristically as follows: first of all, an accurate calculation of a planetary orbit will have to take into account the special-relativistic mass increase

$$m_D = \frac{m}{[1 - (v^2/c^2)]^{1/2}} \tag{2.16}$$

where m is the planet's rest mass. This mass increase contributes to the advance of the planet's perihelion.

The second contribution is even more interesting. The sun is surrounded by a gravitational field. *Associated with this field is an energy density, and--via $E = mc^2$--a mass density that adds to the sun's gravitational force.* We can estimate this effect by making use of the analogy with the known situation of the electrostatic field:

Electrostatic field		Gravitational field	
$V_e = \dfrac{Q}{4\pi\epsilon_0 r}$	Potential	$V_g = -\dfrac{GM}{r}$	(2.17)
$E = -\text{grad } V_e$	Field strength	$g = -\text{grad } V_g$	
$E_e = \dfrac{\epsilon_0 E^2}{2}$	Energy density	$E_g = -\dfrac{g^2}{8\pi G}$	(2.18)

Comparison of these equations shows that the formulas for the gravitational field can be obtained from those of the electrostatic field by substituting the mass M for the charge Q, and the term $-1/4\pi G$ for the dielectric constant ε_0. The sign difference is due to the fact that masses always attract each other, while like charges repel. Substituting the gravitational field strength

$$g = -\frac{MG}{r^2} \times \frac{x}{r} \tag{2.19}$$

into Eq.(2.18) gives the energy density of the gravitational field

$$E_g = -\frac{1}{8\pi} \frac{M^2 G}{r^4} \tag{2.20}$$

(x being the distance vector of the point under consideration from the mass M, $r = |x|$ being the actual distance).

As a result, a planet orbiting the sun on a circle of radius r (Fig. 2.7) feels the influence of a mass M_r that differs from the solar mass M, and is given by

$$M_r = M - \frac{1}{c^2} \int_r^\infty d^3x\, E_g = M + \frac{4\pi}{8\pi} \int_r^\infty \frac{M^2 G}{c^2 r^4} r'^2\, dr' = M + \frac{1}{2} \frac{M^2 G}{rc^2} \tag{2.21}$$

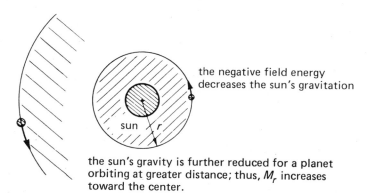

the negative field energy decreases the sun's gravitation

the sun's gravity is further reduced for a planet orbiting at greater distance; thus, M_r increases toward the center.

Fig. 2.7.   Calculation of the perihelion shift.

Note that M_r is larger than M since part of the negative field energy does not act on the planet. Observe also, that for a planet at infinity $(r = \infty)$, $M = M_r$, i.e., it is acted upon by precisely the solar mass M.

The outcome of our analysis is that we have to revise the energy conservation law that is commonly applied in the calculation of planetary orbits:

$$\underbrace{\frac{m_D v^2}{2}}_{\text{Kinetic energy}} - \underbrace{\frac{m_D M_r G}{r}}_{\text{Potential energy}} = E \qquad (2.22)$$

Thus, both the kinetic and potential energy have to be modified. Now in order to estimate the order of magnitude of the corrections that lead to the perihelion shift, we resort to the following trick: For circular orbits (all planetary orbits can be approximated by circles quite closely) we have

$$\frac{mv^2}{r} = \frac{MGm}{r^2} \qquad (2.23)$$

or

$$mv^2 = \frac{MGm}{r} \qquad (2.24)$$

Expanding the square root in Eq.(2.16),

$$\left[m_D \approx m \left(1 + \frac{1}{2} \frac{v^2}{c^2} \right) \right]$$

and inserting the result into the expression for M_r (2.21), we obtain

$$\frac{mv^2}{2} + \frac{m}{4} \frac{v^4}{c^2} - \frac{mMG}{r} - \frac{GmM}{2r} \frac{v^2}{c^2} - \frac{mM^2 G^2}{2r^2 c^2} = E \qquad (2.25)$$

Equation (2.24) can be used to eliminate the velocity (at least approximately) in the small correction term that is proportional to $1/c^2$. Hence

$$\frac{mv^2}{2} - \frac{mMG}{r} - \frac{3mM^2G^2}{4r^2c^2} = E \tag{2.26}$$

Relativistic mass increase and the contribution of the gravitational energy to the solar mass result in corrections of comparable size in the energy conservation law. These relativistic corrections therefore give rise to a supplementary potential

$$V_S \approx -\frac{3}{4}\frac{mM^2G^2}{r^2c^2} \tag{2.27}$$

which must be added to the classical Newtonian potential

$$V_N = -MmG/r$$

We now have the tools to estimate the amount of the perihelion shift caused by the supplementary potential V_S. We know that Newton's potential leads to the classical Kepler ellipse, i.e., to a rotation of the planet's radius vector by 2π between two consecutive passages through the perihelion. On the other hand, the supplementary potential is responsible for an additional small advance, which is precisely the perihelion shift.

The amount of this rotational increment will be related to the usual rotation, 2π, approximately as the supplementary potential is to the Newtonian potential:

$$\frac{\psi}{2\pi} \approx \frac{V_S}{V_N} = \frac{3}{4}\frac{mM^2G^2}{r^2c^2} \bigg/ \frac{mMG}{r}$$

$$\frac{\psi}{2\pi} \approx \frac{3}{4}\frac{MG}{rc^2} = \frac{3}{8}\frac{R}{r} \tag{2.28}$$

This formula is only correct within an order of magnitude. A precise calculation must be based on Einstein's field equations, and will yield the following expression for the perihelion shift:

$$\text{perihelion shift: } \frac{\psi_E}{2\pi} = \frac{3MG}{rc^2} = 1.5\frac{R}{r} \tag{2.29}$$

Actually, our elementary calculation has not been too bad. Not only did we obtain the correct order of magnitude, but we even found the dependence of the perihelion shift on the orbit radius r [for elliptical orbits, r should be replaced by $r = a(1 - e^2)$, e being the eccentricity of the ellipse, a being its major semi-axis]. Note, that this effect is again dependent on the ratio of Schwarzschild radius to radius, the radius this time being that of the planet's orbit, not the sun's. Applied to our own planet earth, e.g., we find that its orbit radius is 150,000,000 km or 200 times the solar radius. Consequently, the perihelion shift is a much smaller effect than the light deflection. On the other hand, it is a cumulative effect, since with orbit after orbit the perihelion advances further and further. This makes it possible to utilize the abundance of astronomical observations made over decades to experimentally verify the phenomenon.

In Table 2.2 we compare the experimental data with the theoretical predictions. Shown is the expected perihelion advance per century. [a is the large semiaxis of the planet's orbit, e the eccentricity, ψ_E the rotation of the perihelion, Eq.(2.29) per revolution, N the number of revolutions per earth century, and ψ_{th} and ψ_{exp} the theoretical and experimentally measured perihelion advances per earth century, resp.]

TABLE 2.2

Planet	$a (10^6$ km)	e	ψ_E	N	ψ_{th}	ψ_{exp}
Mercury	57.91	0.2056	0.1038"	415	43.03	43.11 ± 0.45
Venus	108.21	0.0068	0.058"	149	8.6	8.4 ± 4.8
Earth	149.60	0.0167	0.038"	100	3.8	5.0 ± 1.2
Icarus[a]	161.0	0.827	0.115"	89	10.3	9.8 ± 0.8

[a]Icarus is a planetoid that was discovered in 1949. Of interest is its large eccentricity.

The precision of these observations is quite remarkable when we consider that for the planet Mercury, for example, the measured perihelion shift per century amounts to

$$\psi(\text{Mercury}) = 5600.73 \pm 0.41"$$

Of this value, known nonrelativistic disturbance effects cause a shift of

$$\psi(\text{disturbance}) = 5557.62 \pm 0.20"$$

while only $43.11 \pm 0.45"$ remains as the purely relativistic effect.

The advance of Mercury's perihelion was known to astronomers as early as 1860. Its final explanation through the general theory of relativity in 1915 was the greatest triumph of Einstein's theory.

CHAPTER 3

CURVED SPACE-TIME

Having read the previous chapter the reader might be left with the impression that the general theory of relativity can be understood without any mentioning of Riemann's concept of a curved space-time continuum. Normally, any treatment of the theory revolves around this concept.

It is the purpose of this chapter to establish the connection between our discussion so far and the geometric ideas that underly Einstein's theory. By putting these ideas at the very foundation of his theory, Einstein was rewarded, when in 1915 he was able to calculate the three effects (red shift, light deflection, and perihelion shift) not only qualitatively, but even numerically correct.

THE BEHAVIOR OF CLOCKS

Let us consider the red shift phenomenon from a different point of view. Figure 3.1 depicts two atoms, A and B, which are at rest at separate heights within a gravitational field. The lower atom A emits light that will arrive at the higher atom B slightly red-shifted by the amount

$$\Delta \nu / \nu = \Delta U / c^2 \tag{3.1}$$

where we denote the potential difference between A and B by ΔU as before.

The frequency ν_0 of the light emitted by atom A, or according to Bohr's model the frequency with which the electron orbits A's

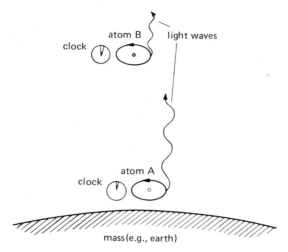

Fig. 3.1. Behavior of atoms (clocks) in a gravity field.

nucleus, can be used as a reference frequency for an atomic clock,
which we shall identify with atom A. Every time the electron
(figuratively speaking) passes a certain point on its orbit, A
emits a wave and thereby advances the hand of its clock by one unit.

We assume that atom B is just a carbon copy of A, also usable
as an atomic clock. In order to compare the speed of both clocks
we now proceed as follows: Every time clock A's hand advances by
1, A sends a signal toward B, e.g., the wave mentioned before. At
B we compare the arriving signals with those emitted by B (i.e.,
with the advance of B's hand). According to Eq.(3.1) the signals
emitted by A will arrive at B with a frequency $\nu_1 = \nu_0 - \Delta\nu$ that
is lower than the frequency of B's signal. Since no information
has been lost on the way from A to B, we must conclude that the
hand of clock A (which moves synchronously with the emission of
A's signal) advances slower than that of clock B.

Our conclusion can be stated as follows:

Clocks go slower in the vicinity of large masses.

While clock B measures a time interval of 1 sec, B emits ν_0
waves but receives only $\nu_1 = \nu_0 - \Delta\nu$ waves from A. In other

words, during the time T_B, clock A will measure the time

$$T_A = \frac{\nu_0 - \Delta\nu}{\nu_0} T_B = \left(1 - \frac{\Delta\nu}{\nu}\right) T_B = \left(1 - \frac{\Delta U}{c^2}\right) T_B \tag{3.2}$$

As a simple example we consider a clock B located "at infinity" (where $U = 0$), while clock A is at rest in a gravitational potential $U = -GM/R$. According to Eq.(2.9), $\Delta\nu/\nu = R/2R$, resulting in

$$T_A = (1 - R/2R) T_B \tag{3.3}$$

Thus, a clock that resides on the sun's surface will be slowed down by a factor of approximately $(\sim 10^{-6})$ when compared to a clock on the earth's surface, where $U \approx 0$.

Let us emphasize once more that atoms can be viewed as clocks (in "atomic clocks" they are actually being used for precise time measurements). *The red shift of spectral lines can then be interpreted as a slowing down of clocks (i.e., atomic frequencies) near heavy masses.*

At the end of this chapter we shall derive the same result in a different manner, at the same time showing that Eq.(3.3) holds for all types of clocks (atoms).

Our discussion so far should also point out the important fact that the discrepancy in clock speed cannot be measured by moving clock A to the same position as clock B. If we do that, then the potential difference between A and B vanishes ($\Delta U = 0$), and both clocks will go equally fast. If they did not, we would be dealing with two differently constructed clocks, contrary to our assumptions.

In order to measure the effect given by Eq.(3.3) we must rather proceed as follows: first, both clocks are being compared and synchronized at the same location. Then we transport clock A into a gravitational field, leaving it there for some time. Finally, clock A is brought back to clock B's position, and both

clocks are being compared. At that point, the time difference
given by (3.3) will be noticeable.

An experiment based on precisely this procedure was actually
conducted in 1971.

THE HAFELE-KEATING EXPERIMENT

A few decades ago it appeared to be impossible to measure the
influence of the earth's gravitational field on clocks, since
clocks with the necessary accuracy were not available. By about
1960 the precision of cesium clocks had been increased to such a
degree that even subtle irregularities in the earth's rotation
could be detected. In due time a number of proposals were made
for the installation of such clocks into space satellites, and
there were even preparations for the measurements of Eq.(3.2).
Figure 3.2 shows the experiment in which a reference clock A
resting on the earth's surface is being compared with a clock B
located in a satellite.

Since clock B is further away from earth than clock A (i.e.,
at a lower gravitational potential), it will go faster than A. As
long as the satellite does not fly too high, we can set the potential difference to $\Delta U = gh$, where H is the satellite's altitude.
Equation (3.2) then becomes

$$T_A = \left(1 - \frac{gH}{c^2}\right) T_B \tag{3.4}$$

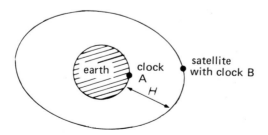

Fig. 3.2.   *Measurements of the speed of clocks located in
satellites.*

This result, however, is based on the assumption that both clocks A and B are at rest. Because of the earth's rotation as well as the satellite's motion this assumption cannot be maintained. Instead, we must take into account another effect: according to special relativity, a clock that moves with velocity v will go slower by a factor of $(1 - v^2/c^2)^{1/2}$ with respect to a motionless clock. Consequently, the time actually measured by clock A has to be revised to give

$$t_A = \left(1 - \frac{v_A^2}{c^2}\right)^{1/2} T_A \approx \left(1 - \frac{v_A^2}{2c^2}\right) T_A \tag{3.5}$$

where $v_A \approx 1667$ km/h is the earth's rotational speed. Similarly, if v_B is the satellite's orbital speed, we find the revised time measured by clock B to be

$$t_B \approx \left(1 - \frac{v_B^2}{2c^2}\right) T_B \tag{3.6}$$

Substituting (3.5) and (3.6) into Eq.(3.4) yields[1]

$$t_B \approx \left(1 - \frac{v_B^2}{2c^2}\right) T_B \approx \left(1 + \frac{gH}{c^2}\right)\left(1 - \frac{v_B^2}{c^2}\right) T_A$$

$$\approx \left(1 + \frac{gH}{c^2} + \frac{v_A^2}{2c^2} - \frac{v_B^2}{2c^2}\right) t_A \tag{3.7}$$

As we see, a comparison between the earth clock and the satellite clock involves both the special relativistic time dilatation as well as the gravitational effect.

While preparations for sophisticated and expensive satellite experiments made only slow progress, two physicists quietly plotted a sort of "scientific surprise attack." Joseph Hafele

---

[1] We are using the approximation $(1 - x)^{-1} \approx 1 + x$ for $x \ll 1$.

(at the Research Department of the Caterpillar Tractor Company, Peoria, Illinois) and Richard Keating (at the Time Service Division of the U.S. Naval Observatory, Washington, D.C.) were convinced that cesium clocks had reached an accuracy that would make it possible to measure the influence of speed and gravity on clocks in ordinary commercial airplanes.

Equipped with four cesium clocks the two men set out in October 1971 to fly around the earth in an easterly and westerly direction (see Fig. 3.3). The predicted relativistic time differences are listed in Table 3.1. The table contains the predicted time differences (in nanoseconds) between the reference clock A located in Washington, D.C., and clock B aboard the airplane. A precise knowledge of altitudes, flight times, etc. was essential for making accurate predictions (note the indicated error bounds in Table 3.1).

According to the table, the expected effect of gravity on the clocks is roughly the same for both flight directions. The "flying" clocks feel a lesser gravitational potential, and hence go faster than the reference clock on earth.

In order to investigate the various effects on the different clocks, we choose an inertial system that moves with the earth on its orbit around the sun, but does not take part in the earth's

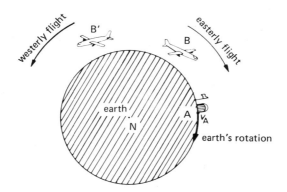

Fig. 3.3. The clocks used in the Hafele-Keating experiment.

TABLE 3.1.   Predictions of Relativistic Time Differences (nsec).

Effect	Easterly flight B	Westerly flight B´
Gravitation	144 ± 14	179 ± 18
Speed	-184 ± 18	96 ± 10
Sum	-40 ± 23	275 ± 21

TABLE 3.2.   Experimental Results of Hafele and Keating.

Serial number of the clock	Easterly flight	Westerly flight
120	-57	277
361	-74	284
408	-55	266
447	-51	266
Mean	-59 ± 10	273 ± 7
Theory	-40 ± 23	275 ± 21

rotation. Viewed from this observation system, clock B during its easterly flight moves faster than the reference clock A, and by special relativity is slower than A (by -184 nsec). However, the gravitational field counteracts this effect, and the resulting slowdown is reduced to only -40 nsec. During the westerly flight, both speed and gravitational effects add to each other, resulting in a speedup of clock B by about 275 nsec. Table 3.2 shows the results (in nanoseconds) of those flights. The experiments were conducted on regular scheduled flights with Pan Am, TWA, and American Airlines, and did not require any extensive preparations.

It is noteworthy that a simple-minded experiment like that of Hafele and Keating brought about a verification of the theoretical predictions to within 10%. For the first time, ordinary macroscopic clocks had demonstrated the relativistic influence of gravity on clocks, as well as the special-relativistic "clock paradox." While this book was being written, astronomers were still waiting for results from the planned satellite experiments!

Between September 1975 and January 1976 a team from the University of Maryland conducted an even more accurate experiment. The speed of atomic clocks traveling aboard airplanes at 30,000 feet was compared against the speed of ground-based atomic clocks.

After a number of test flights the team undertook five flights each lasting for 15 hours.

This experiment required lengthy preparations. Three atomic clocks were installed in the plane while three clocks remained on the ground. All six clocks were packed into special containers, which served as protection against vibrations, magnetic fields, and variations of temperature and air pressure. Both, the airplane and the ground station were equipped with a computer that stored and analyzed the time measurements given by the clocks as well as all the flight data. While the airplane traveled along a fixed route, its course was constantly monitored by a laser beam. It was therefore possible to update the plane's position and speed at every instant.

The actual time measurements were conducted in two ways: first, through direct comparison of the clocks before and after the flight (time $\approx$ 20 h); secondly, with the help of laser impulses. These impulses, lasting 0.1 nsec were emitted by the ground station, registered and reflected by the airplane, and received again by the ground station. The time at which the signal arrived at the plane was recorded by the plane's atomic clocks and stored in the computer. On the ground, the same arrival time was computed as the mean value of the times when the signal was emitted and received by the station. This procedure allowed constant monitoring of the increasing time discrepancy between the two sets of clocks during the flight.

Figure 3.4 shows this discrepancy graphically. Due to gravitational effects the airplane's clocks go faster during flight, the resulting time difference being ~53 nsec. The relativistic

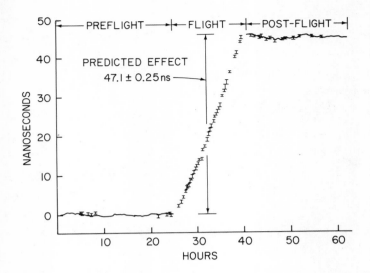

Fig. 3.4. Time comparisons between the atomic clocks in the airplane and on the ground (Maryland experiment). During the pre-flight and postflight phases both clocks show the same running speed. During the flight the clocks in the plane are nearly 47 nsec fast.

effect based on the airplane's motion, on the other hand, tends to slow down the airplane clocks. In order to minimize this relativistic effect, older turboprop planes were used, which only reached a speed of up to 500 km/h. The resulting relativistic time dilatation was -6 nsec; the overall time difference was therefore 53 - 6 = 47 nsec. In Fig. 3.5 we compare the theoretical time deviations as calculated from the flight data against the experimental data. If we take into account all five flights and all possible error sources we reach the following result:

$$\frac{\text{measured effect}}{\text{calculated effect}} = 0.987 \pm 0.016$$

Atomic clocks have therefore succeeded in verifying the relativistic effects of gravitation as well as of speed with an accuracy of 1.6%:

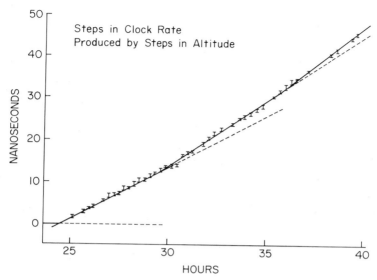

*Fig. 3.5. Comparison of the experimental data with the theo-
retical prediction. The influence of the gravitational potential
dominates. The curve shows two breaks in the slope corresponding
to altitude changes of the airplane.*

*Atomic clocks can verify relativistic time effects to an
accuracy of nearly 1%.*

Problem 3.1: The Hafele-Keating Experiment

Check the order of magnitude of the entries in Table 3.1 by
setting $v_B = v_A \pm v_F$ in Eq. (3.7), where $v_F \approx 900$ km/h is an average flight speed. For H, substitute some typical flight altitudes. What is the required clock precision if the relativistic
effect is to be measured with an accuracy of 1%?

Problem 3.2: The Twin Paradox

The effect of speed on clocks is often applied to human
beings. Thus, an astronaut traveling close to the speed of light
should have aged less after his return to earth than his twin
brother who remained on earth. Do you feel that human beings can

be considered as clocks or do you see any problems? How would the
effects of time dilatation on humans be noticeable? At which
order of magnitude would such effects be measurable?

THE BEHAVIOR OF MEASURING RODS

The influence of the gravitational potential on the speed of
clocks could be derived from the equivalence principle. On the
other hand, the behavior of measuring rods in a gravitational
field cannot be deduced that easily. In this case we can only
study the result that is predicted by general relativity.

Einstein's field equations for gravitation (which are analogous to Maxwell's field equations for electromagnetism) predict
not only the gravitational effect on clocks [Eq.(3.2)] but also an
equivalent effect on measuring rods (see Fig. 3.6). Here is the
predicted effect, resulting from general relativity theory:

*A measuring stick located in a gravitational field will
shrink by a factor* $1 - \Delta U/c^2$, *so that its length becomes*

$$L_A = \left(1 - \frac{\Delta U}{c^2}\right)L_B \qquad \qquad sign\ of\ \Delta U\,? \qquad \qquad (3.8)$$

In particular, a measuring stick that has length L_B when infinitely far away from any masses will shrink to length

$$L_A = \left(1 - \frac{R}{2R}\right)L_B \qquad \qquad (3.9)$$

when at distance R from a mass.

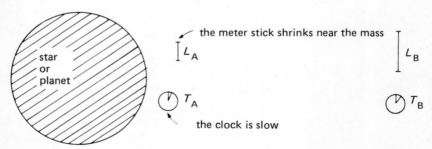

the meter stick shrinks near the mass

L_A L_B

star
or
planet

T_A T_B

the clock is slow

Fig. 3.6. Effect of gravity on clocks and meter sticks.

The shrinking of a measuring rod cannot be detected by transporting a second rod to the location of the first one and comparing their lengths. The second rod would shrink by the same
amount as the first, and so would any other rods that are moved to
the same point in space. The situation is analogous to the detection of the slowdown of clocks, which could not be achieved by
transporting reference clocks to the same location, since the
gravitational effect applies universally to all clocks.

Just as we were able to detect the speed discrepancy of distant clocks, we shall show that it is possible (at least in principle) to measure the gravitational effect on measuring sticks.

Our method is based on the fact that the shrinkage increases
as the stick is moved closer to a mass. Figure 3.7 indicates how
the spatial geometry in the vicinity of the sun can be obtained
through measuring rods. The figure shows a plane that cuts the
sun as well as the surrounding space into two equal parts. On
this plane we see a number of measuring rods that are intended to
measure the radius and circumference of a circle. Figure 3.7
shows clearly that more measuring sticks are needed to measure the

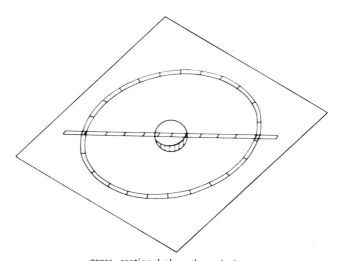

cross—sectional plane through the sun

Fig. 3.7. Geometry near the sun.

radius than are normally needed for a circle with this circumference. Measuring the radius a and circumference U by the number of measuring rods (as is normally done), we find a ratio $U/a < 2\pi$.

This result has two interpretations: We can maintain the idea that the surface of the cut is a plane in which measuring rods shrink as they approach the sun. This amounts to axiomatically fixing the structure of space to be Euclidean. We then have to conduct experiments that will give us information about the gravitational effect on the lengths of measuring rods.

There is an alternative interpretation, which for many purposes is much more suitable. Since the shrinking of measuring sticks cannot be measured by bringing several rods to the same location, we are free to axiomatically decree that all rods have the identical length, *independent of their location*.

This latter interpretation does not provide information about the behavior of measuring rods, but reveals something about the geometrical structure of space. Since $U/a < 2\pi$, we know that Euclidean geometry cannot be valid on our cut surface. Instead, we can describe the metric relationships on that surface by using Riemann's geometry, which is a generalization of Euclid's geometry. In this framework, the result $U/a < 2\pi$ simply tells us that the surface is not plane (Euclidean) but warped (Riemannian) (see Fig. 3.8). This is the famous concept of curved space that is closely tied to general relativity: Locally, space (or spacetime) is a flat Euclidean (or Minkowski) space, permitting special relativity to be applied to free-falling reference systems. Globally, however, space is a (warped) Riemannian space whose curvature is determined by the mass distribution.

We ought to mention that most works on general relativity present the point of view shown in Fig. 3.8b. It is more common to deal with the warped Riemannian space concept since the idea of shrinking measuring rods and slower clocks becomes overly complicated and confusing when dealing with dynamic, i.e., with time-varying, space-time metrics.

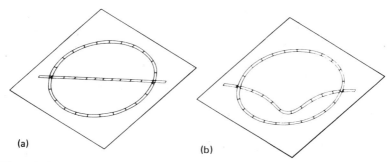

Fig. 3.8. (a) Euclidean space and shrinking meter sticks, or (b) curved = Riemannian space and constant-length meter sticks.

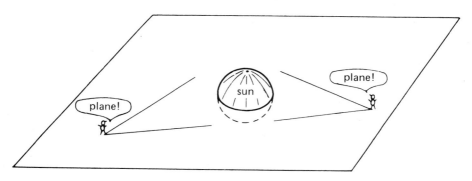

Fig. 3.9. Observers located on the cut surface will view the surface as a (Euclidean) plane.

Since the concept of curved space will be the basis for everything that follows, we should spend a few moments contemplating the meaning of Fig. 3.8. The sun's vicinity had been cut into two identical parts by the surface. Symmetry considerations dictate that the cut surface must be like a plane, in that it cannot be curved "up" or "down." Observers on that surface will have the visual impression of standing on a plane (Fig. 3.9). However, if they measure geometric proportions on that surface, they will find

that $U/a < 2\pi$. In order to provide a simple physical model for
this result, they can make use of Fig. 3.8b.[2]

Problem 3.3: What Is Plane?

What would be your answer to the question: Is the cut surface
a plane or not? Can such a question, which is asked frequently in
a slightly different form, be answered easily?

LIGHT DEFLECTION AND SPACE-TIME GEOMETRY

The effect that lets measuring rods shrink in the vicinity of
the sun, in other words, the curvature of space, is the ultimate
cause for the factor 2 in the light deflection formula.

According to Fermat's principle, a beam of light will follow
a trajectory that will lead from point A to point B in the fastest
manner (see Fig. 3.10). The slowing of clocks near the sun, however, will result in an apparent reduction of the speed of light

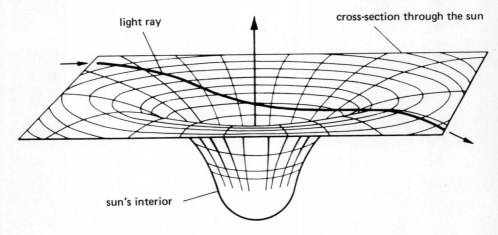

Fig. 3.10. Behavior of light rays near the sun.

[2]*In other words, they locally (where the space is essentially
Euclidean) construct a curved surface with the same geometrical
relations that exist on the cut surface through the sun.*

at the same location. (This reduction is, of course, not noticeable by a local observer since measurements of the speed of lights
with slow clocks will still result in the same value as everywhere
else!) Due to this apparent reduction of the speed of light near
the sun, the beam of light will try to avoid the vicinity of the
sun in order to reach point B as fast as possible.

Consequently, the light ray will travel along a curved path,
analogous to the well-known curved paths that result in media with
variable refraction coefficients (e.g., in gases with variable
density; this is the cause of a *fata morgana*).

The slowdown of clocks, however, provides only one-half of the
explanation for the light deflection. The other half is explained
through the effect of shrinking measuring rods. According to Fig.
3.10, the spatial curvature near the sun causes a further reduction of the speed of light, due to the longer distance that must
be traversed. The total reduction of the speed of light gives
rise to the factor 2, which separates Einstein's theory from
Newton's.

During the last couple of years a further experiment has become feasible that provides a direct demonstration of the spatial
curvature, or equivalently, the shrinking of measuring rods as
shown in Fig. 3.10.

THE SHAPIRO EXPERIMENT

In 1965, I. I. Shapiro suggested a new test of general relativity, which became possible through the progress made in radar
technology and the design of more accurate atomic clocks. In
principle, Shapiro's experiment is quite simple: a radar signal
is sent from earth toward Venus or some other planet, where it is
reflected and arrives back at earth. The time it takes to travel
from earth to Venus to earth is accurately measured. According to
the discussion in the previous paragraph, the time of the signal
will be larger than expected by Newton's theory, if the signal has
to pass near the sun's edge on its way from earth to Venus and

back.   The slowdown of clocks as well as the increased length of the (curved) light path near the sun (Fig. 3.10) contribute to this effect.[3]

In order to calculate this increase in signal time, we shall take the viewpoint expressed in Fig. 3.8a. The shrinking of measuring sticks near the sun, combined with the slowdown of clocks will result in an apparent reduction of the effective speed of light:

$$c_{eff} = \left(1 - \frac{R}{2r}\right)^2 c \approx \left(1 - \frac{R}{r}\right)c \tag{3.10}$$

Let us emphasize once more that c_{eff} cannot be obtained through measurements conducted in the sun's vicinity, since the influence of the gravitational field on measuring rods and clocks will just compensate the effect (3.10), resulting in precisely the normal value c for the speed of light. The decrease of the effective speed of light can only be observed through comparison with measuring instruments that are located outside the gravitational field. This is precisely what is done when the signal time is measured on earth, for the earth's gravitational field is about 200 times weaker than the field near the sun's edge. We may therefore neglect the earth's field when compared against the sun's. Using Einstein's theory, we can estimate the traveling time t_E of a light signal in the solar system:

$$t_E = \int \frac{dx}{c_{eff}} = \int \frac{dx}{c(1 - R/r)} \approx \int \frac{dx}{c} + \frac{R}{c} \int \frac{dx}{r} = t_N + \Delta t \tag{3.11}$$

In this equation dx is the arc length element along the trajectory of the light signal. Thus, the expected travel time according to Newton would be $t_N = \int dx/c$. For a light signal that passes very

---

[3]All our results, which applied to light signals, are equally valid for radar signals, which have only a slightly different frequency.

close to the sun's edge, we obtain a relativistic time increment:

$$\Delta t = \left(\frac{2R}{c}\right)\!\!\int_{-a_E}^{a_V} \frac{dx}{\left(R^2 + x^2\right)^{1/2}} \tag{3.12}$$

where a_E and a_V are the distances of earth and Venus from the sun, respectively, and where the factor 2 reflects the fact that the signal makes a round trip (see Fig. 3.11). Evaluation of the integral gives:

$$\Delta t = \left(\frac{2R}{c}\right) \ln\!\left(\frac{\left(R^2 + a_E^2\right)^{1/2} + a_E}{\left(R^2 + a_V^2\right)^{1/2} - a_V}\right) \approx \frac{2R}{c}\ln\!\left(\frac{4a_E a_V}{R^2}\right) \tag{3.13}$$

Here we have used the assumption $R \ll a_E, a_V$, and then expanded the square roots:

$$\left(R^2 + a_E^2\right)^{1/2} \approx a_E \;;$$

$$\left(R^2 + a_V^2\right)^{1/2} \approx a_V + \frac{R^2}{2a_V}$$

Using Table 3.2, we find

$$\Delta t = \left(\frac{2R}{c}\right) \times 11.9 = \left(\frac{2}{c}\right) \times 36\ \text{km} = 240\ \mu\text{sec} \tag{3.14}$$

In other words, the increased travel time of the light signal (240 μsec) is equivalent to an apparent increase in the distance from earth to Venus of 36 km.

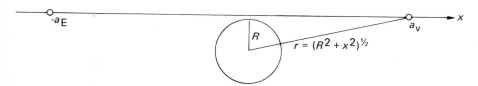

Fig. 3.11. Calculation of the Shapiro effect.

Figure 3.12 contains Shapiro's measurements of Δt taken in 1970. The time increment Δt is presented as a function of time τ. The value $\tau = 0$ corresponds to the situation depicted in Fig. 3.11, i.e., the sun is between earth and Venus ("upper conjunction"). For $\tau \neq 0$, the time dilatation Δt decreases since earth and Venus move on, causing the radar signal to by-pass the sun at increasing distances.

According to Shapiro's experiments, Einstein's formula (3.13) is valid to within 3%, thus providing another verification of the curved space-time concept of general relativity.

Since the relativistic effect (3.14) corresponds to an apparent change in distance of 36 km, a measurement of 3% accuracy means a determination of the distance between earth and Venus to within 1 km! This is a lower bound for any measuring technique since the surface irregularities of Venus prevent more accurate distance measurements.

For the sake of completeness we ought to mention that the travel time of radio signals was also measured by the two

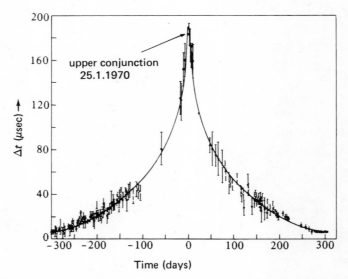

Fig. 3.12. Shapiro's measurements of the delay of a radar signal being reflected by Venus.

spacecrafts Mariner 6 and Mariner 7. Again, they verified
Einstein's prediction (3.13) to within 3%.

CURVED SPACE-TIME AND INTUITION

During the first few years following Einstein's publication of
the general theory of relativity, it was particularly his concept
of a curved space that created quite a stir in the scientific
community. Can such a space be imagined or comprehended? Is not
space (a priori) prerequisite to any physical knowledge? If so,
how can the structure of space then possibly be determined by
means of empirical observations (a posteriori)?

The experiments that have been conducted during recent years
have demonstrated that Einstein's concept of curved space-time
agrees with experience to a high degree of accuracy. In the case
of our sun the discrepancies from Euclidean geometry, however, are
of the order of 10^{-6}, and therefore only perceptible by highly
sensitive measuring instruments. Let us imagine, though, that we
live on a neutron star, or perhaps even in the vicinity of a black
hole. In Chapter 4 it will be shown that for those objects the
deviation from a flat Euclidean space approaches a magnitude of 1.

In this situation the curvature of space-time would be noticeable not only to sensitive instruments but would become apparent
in everyday experiences. How would life be in such a strongly
curved space? Our description of this imaginary experiment will
also answer the question whether we can imagine curved space.
After all, "to imagine," simply means to describe those sensations
that are caused by living in a strongly curved space.

This is not so hard. All we have to do is to magnify the experiments discussed so far by a factor of a million, thus moving
them out of the realm of precision measurements into the world of
everyday experiences.

What are the ramifications caused by the slowing down of
clocks near the star? The closer we live to the surface of a neutron star, the less we age. We have found a fountain of youth:

the cellar of a house, or an underground mine. There, all events seem to happen in slow motion, but only when viewed from a higher vantage point, say a mountain or skyscraper. If I live near the surface, I do not notice that time is slowed down. The slowdown affects everything and everybody equally, and can therefore not be detected by me as long as I am part of that "low-altitude" neighborhood. Consequently, my prolonged life is of no use to me: its apparent length as well as the number of events that fill it are no different than anywhere else.

However, if I look up to the "mountain people" or to the poor people who must live in the highest portions of the skyscrapers, then I notice that everything seems to take place at a frantic speed. Tasks that must be taken care of quickly will be handled in those higher regions. If I want, I can also drive to a mountain top. Here I do my day's work, and return home only minutes after I had left. As far as I am concerned though, I have worked a full day, and feel tired accordingly. Also, I have aged by a day in contrast to my wife, who stayed home, and is only a few minutes older when I return!

Life on a neutron star also awaits us with a whole caleidoscope of new color phenomena, which are caused by the red shift effect. A red apple that lies on the ground becomes green when I lift it up: it was only the red shift that made the apple appear to be ripe!

Traffic lights on a neutron star are particularly simple. They consist of three red lamps that are located at different heights (Fig. 3.13). The light of the uppermost lamp will appear green due to the blue shift, while that of the middle lamp will appear yellow!

Life on the neutron star also offers a variety of other interesting optical effects that are the result of the curvature of light rays.

The light deflection is so strong that we can perceive objects that are located on the other side of the star. These objects

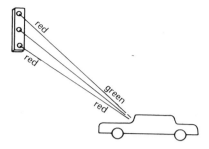

Fig. 3.13. Traffic lights on a neutron star.

will appear distorted into a ring, taking on the appearance of a
halo (see Figs. 3.14 and 3.15). The deflection of light may even
become so extreme that we can look around the star since the light
is warped into a circle by the gravitational field.

Normally, the optical effects are not as spectacular as those
just described. However, all kinds of optical distortions and
illusions are part of every day life on a neutron star, and we
perceive a world full of fata morganas.

We probably would not even be conscious of these effects. On
earth we can also find optical phenomena, of which we are normally
not even aware. Objects vary their color under different lighting, and vary their shape if viewed from different angles and
distances. Nevertheless, we can identify them at a glance. This
is a remarkable achievement of our visual perception, and is of
greatest importance for our daily life: a lion at great distance
will not appear as a small kitten that grows to frightening proportions as it approaches us. We actually perceive it as a lion
independent of the distance and the lighting. Clearly, this
property of our visual perception is of extreme practical value
(at least, if one lives in Africa).

Our space perception is not determined by spatial relations,
but rather by identifiable and familiar objects. It was not by
accident that the spatial perspective was "discovered" during the
renaissance.

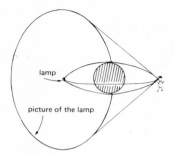

Fig. 3.14. *A simple lamp appears as a ring of light around the star due to the extreme light deflection.*

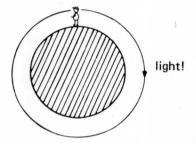

light!

Fig. 3.15. *On a neutron star you do not need a mirror to see the back of your head.*

It is likely, that from the beginning epistemological arguments played an important role in the development of the natural sciences. What is straight, what is curved? Simple questions for physicists on earth--at least on a naive level. A source of never-ending controversies for physicists on neutron stars. Mathematical models that describe a whole multitude of phenomena in simple concepts come about very slowly. An example is the model of curved space-time (Fig. 3.10).

Problem 3.4: Once Again: What Is Straight?

Take another look at Problem 2.2. Are you satisfied with your first answer, or has our discussion in this chapter resulted in some new aspects? Take into consideration the answer to Problem 3.3!

Problem 3.5: Life on a Neutron Star

What would be the every-day effects of shrinking measuring rods on neutron stars?

Problem 3.6: Effects of Spatial Curvature
on Neutron Stars

Try to graphically represent the effects caused by shrinking measuring rods on neutron stars.

Problem 3.7. Civilizations on Neutron Stars

Try to describe the cultural history of a civilization that lives on a neutron star. How, in your opinion, did geometry and physics develop?

CLOCKS IN A GRAVITATIONAL FIELD--ANOTHER VIEWPOINT

The behavior of clocks will be studied from a different point of view, emphasizing the connection with the equivalence principle.

Let us consider two clocks, A and B, located in an elevator that accelerates upwards. Let C be a motionless reference clock (Fig. 3.16). At the moment when clock B passes clock C, it has a speed v_B, and due to the special relativistic time dilatation, B will go slower when observed from C, i.e., B will show the time

$$T_B = T_C \left(1 - \frac{v_B^2}{c^2} \right)^{1/2} \tag{3.15}$$

A few moments later, clock A passes C with a velocity $v_A > v_B$, since the elevator is accelerating. The time intervals measured by A, but viewed from C are

$$T_A = T_C \left(1 - \frac{v_A^2}{c^2} \right)^{1/2} \tag{3.16}$$

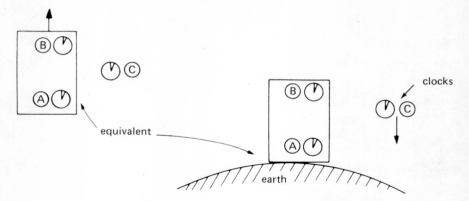

Fig. 3.16. *Using the equivalence principle to study the effect of gravity on clocks.*

The second part of Fig. 3.16 shows the analogous situation based on the equivalence principle. Here the elevator stands still in a gravitational field, while clock C is in a free fall. As before, clock C is located in an inertial system; consequently, Eqs.(3.15) and (3.16) are still valid. Division of both equations and expansion of the square roots yields

$$\frac{T_B}{T_A} = \frac{\left(1 - v_B^2/c^2\right)^{1/2}}{\left(1 - v_A^2/c^2\right)^{1/2}} \approx \frac{1 - v_B^2/2c^2}{1 - v_A^2/2c^2} \approx 1 + \frac{v_A^2 - v_B^2}{2c^2} \tag{3.17}$$

The free fall velocity of C can be obtained from energy conservation:

$$\frac{v^2}{2} + U(x) = E = \text{const} \tag{3.18}$$

Hence,

$$\frac{v_A^2 - v_B^2}{2c^2} = \frac{U(x_B) - U(x_A)}{c^2} = -\frac{\Delta U}{c^2}$$

or

$$T_B = T_A \left(1 - \frac{\Delta U}{c^2} \right)$$ (3.19)

This is precisely the result we obtained earlier [Eq. (3.2)].

CHAPTER 4

STARS AND PLANETS

One of the key results from Chapters 2 and 3 states that relativistic effects are proportional to the ratio of Schwarzschild radius to stellar radius, this ratio being of the order of 10^{-6} in the case of our sun.

What determines the ratio R/R? In order to answer that question, we must investigate the theory of stellar structures, since R/R is clearly dependent on the composition of stars, in our case, the sun.

In this chapter we are therefore going to cover the elementary theory of the evolution and inner composition of stars. In the course of our study we shall also discover a number of close links between astrophysics and elementary particle physics.

STELLAR EVOLUTION AND THE STABILITY CONDITION

Elementary statistical physics teaches us that every gas tends to fill its available volume uniformly. This result, however, does not hold true in full generality; only under laboratory conditions is it valid. In fact, gas clouds of cosmic size tend to be unstable due to gravitational effects, and rather than filling the container--the universe--uniformly, they contract to smaller volumes and eventually form stars (Fig. 4.1). The most fascinating part of astrophysics deals with the various phases of this instability: the contraction, and the onset of nuclear burning. Many details of these phases could only recently be explained satisfactorily.

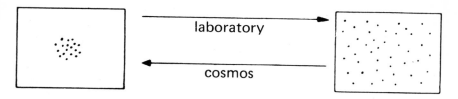

Fig. 4.1. Gas clouds in the laboratory and in the cosmos.

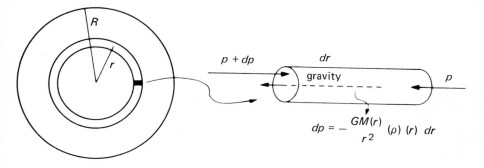

Fig. 4.2. Calculation of the pressure in the star's interior.

While the onset of instability is determined by the Jeans
criterion (see problems 4.2 and 4.3), our concern is with the
question: when does the contraction of the gas cloud stop, i.e.,
when does it reach equilibrium?

According to Fig. 4.2, stellar equilibrium is maintained by an
interior pressure that exactly counteracts the force of gravity.
The pressure increase dp in the star's interior is determined by
the condition that it must be capable of supporting an additional
spherical shell of thickness dr. Now pressure is by definition
force per unit area, and so we have to calculate the weight of a
pillar of cross-sectional area 1 and height dr, and then set this
weight equal to dp:

$$dp = -\frac{GM(r)}{r^2} \rho \; dr \tag{4.1}$$

Here ρ is the density and $M(r)$ is that portion of the star's mass
contained within a radius r:

$$M(r) = 4\pi \int_0^r r'^2 \, \rho(r') \, dr' \qquad (4.2)$$

(According to a well-known theorem of mechanics the outer shells do not contribute to the force that acts on the volume element under consideration.)

Equation (4.1) is a differential equation for pressure as a function of radius:

$$\frac{dp}{dr} = -\frac{GM(r)}{r^2} \, \rho(r) \qquad (4.3)$$

In order to calculate a *realistic* stellar model we must take into account the fact that the density in the interior of a star is not a constant but varies with radius: $\rho = \rho(r)$. Thus, the differential equation (4.3), which determines the interior pressure, contains a further unknown: density as a function of radius. We therefore require one more equation to solve (4.3). This additional equation is the equation of state, which expresses pressure as a function of density and temperature:

$$p = p(\rho, T) \qquad (4.4)$$

Equations (4.2)-(4.4) govern the stellar structure according to Newton's gravitational theory (see Fig. 4.3).

In order to solve (4.3), we shall approximate the differential quotient dp/dr by the difference quotient $-p/R$, where p is a mean

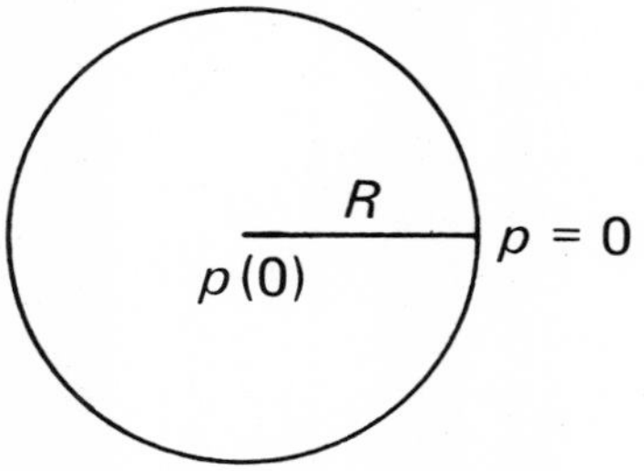

$$\frac{dp}{dr} \approx \frac{p(R) - p(0)}{R}$$

$$= -\frac{p(0)}{R} \approx -\frac{p}{R}$$

Fig. 4.3. Calculation of the pressure in the star's interior.

pressure in the star, and R is the star's radius. In addition, we shall approximate

$$GM(r)\frac{\rho(r)}{r^2} \approx \frac{GM\rho}{R^2} \tag{4.5}$$

where the (mean) density ρ is related to the total mass M of the star according to

$$M = 4\pi \int_0^R \rho(r)r^2\,dr \approx \rho R^3 \tag{4.6}$$

Substituting these approximations into Eq.(4.3) yields

$$\frac{p}{R} \approx \frac{GM}{R^2}\rho \tag{4.7}$$

Division by $\rho c^2/R$ finally gives

$$\frac{p}{\rho c^2} \approx \frac{GM}{Rc^2} \tag{4.8}$$

The right-hand side of Eq.(4.8) is precisely the ratio of Schwarzschild radius R to stellar radius R, if we neglect the factor 2. The equilibrium condition therefore becomes

$$\frac{p}{\rho c^2} \approx \frac{R}{R} \tag{4.9}$$

This fundamental relationship expresses the fact that the ratio R/R is of the same order of magnitude as the ratio of mean pressure to mean rest energy density (ρc^2) inside the star. The ratio $p/\rho c^2$, in turn, is determined by the equation of state, which can be written in the following (dimensionless) form:

$$\frac{p}{\rho c^2} = f(\rho, T) \tag{4.10}$$

Here the function $f(\rho, T)$ characterizes the stellar matter.

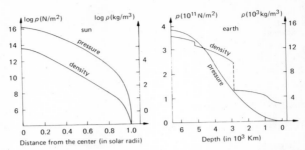

Fig. 4.4.   Pressure and density in sun and earth.

Our simple-minded approximation shows that the theory of stellar composition reduces to finding the function f of density and temperature.

Problem 4.1:   Density and Pressure Inside Earth and Sun

Use Eq.(4.9) to compute the mean pressure in the interior of earth and sun. Compare the answers with the standard models given in Fig. 4.4.

THE MASS DEFECT

Before discussing the function f, we want to explain the central importance of the ratio R/R from a different point of view.

A gas cloud that contracts to form a star releases energy--the gravitational binding energy. In order to estimate its order of magnitude (again we ignore exact numerical factors), we view the star as being composed of two hemispheres each of mass $M_0/2$. Now we know that at a distance R the gravitational potential of a mass $M_0/2$ is given by

$$V(R) \approx -GM_0/2R \qquad (4.11)$$

(this formula is actually valid only for spherical masses, but is a good approximation even for our hemisphere). The gravitational binding energy E released when the second hemisphere of mass $M_0/2$ is brought to distance R (R being close to the radius of the

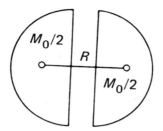

Fig. 4.5. Calculation of the binding energy of a spherical mass.

spheres; see Fig. 4.5) will be

$$E \approx -V(R)\,\frac{M_0}{2} \approx \frac{GM_0^2}{4R} \approx \frac{GM_0^2}{R} \tag{4.12}$$

This result reflects only the order of magnitude of the binding energy E, since we have discarded the factor 1/4 (the correct factor would have been 3/5). Precise numerical results, however, are not necessary for the ensuing discussion.

Equation (4.12) enables us to compute the energy that is released at star formation for different types of stars. For the purpose of gaining a better insight into the results we shall shift our attention from the binding energy E to the mass defect ΔM, which is related to E according to Einstein's formula

$$E = \Delta M c^2$$

During the formation phase, the mass ΔM is radiated away in the form of light, neutrinos, etc. Thus, the star will end up with a mass M that is smaller than the mass M_0 of the initial gas cloud:

$$M = M_0 - \Delta M = M_0 - \frac{E}{c^2} \approx M_0 - \frac{GM_0^2}{Rc^2} \tag{4.13}$$

This also explains the negative sign in Eq.(2.20). Using the Schwarzschild radius, Eq.(4.13) can be simplified further:

$$M \approx M_0 \left(1 - \frac{GM_0}{Rc^2} \right) \approx M_0 \left(1 - \frac{R}{R} \right) \tag{4.14}$$

According to Eq.(4.14), the mass defect $\Delta M = M_0 - M$ is given by

$$\text{mass defect} \quad \frac{\Delta M}{M_0} \approx \frac{R}{R} \tag{4.15}$$

The values of R/R listed in Table 2.1 can therefore also be interpreted as the relative mass defect that is radiated away when the particular object is formed.

Table 2.1 tells us that the gravitational mass defect of our sun is approximately 10^{-6}. In other words, the binding energy can be neglected when compared to the nuclear energy which leads to mass defects of 1%. This fact explains why scientists in the nineteenth century predicted a relatively short lifetime for the sun. While the sun can sustain its radiation of $L_0 \approx 10^{26}$ W due to nuclear energy for about 10^9 years, it would emit radiation only for a couple of million years based on the gravitational binding energy (Kelvin's contraction time).

Even in white dwarfs the nuclear energy dominates over the binding energy, and it is only for neutron stars that the nuclear energy falls behind the gravitational binding energy. During the formation of a neutron star (pulsar) several percent of the mass of the original interstellar gas can be transformed into energy. Since the mass of a neutron star is $M \approx 10^{30}$ kg, which is equivalent to an energy $E \approx 10^{47}$ J, we can expect an energy output of approximately 10^{45} J during the "birth" of a neutron star. This is considered to be the energy source of a super nova.

Our results so far may be summarized in a remarkable chain of equations: light deflection δ, red shift $\Delta\nu/\nu$, and mass defect $\Delta M/M$ of a star are given by the ratio R/R. The equilibrium condition for a star shows further that R/R is determined by $p/\rho c^2$, and

$p/\rho c^2$ finally is dependent on the equation of state $f(\rho, T)$:

$$\delta \approx \frac{\Delta \nu}{\nu} \approx \frac{\Delta M}{M} \approx \frac{R}{R} \approx \frac{p}{\rho c^2} = f(\rho, T) \tag{4.16}$$

Problem 4.2: The Jeans Criterion

A cloud of gas becomes unstable when its gravitational energy surpasses the thermal energy of the molecules, i.e., if

$$E_B \approx \frac{GM^2}{R} > E_{Kin} = \left(\frac{3}{2} kT\right)\frac{M}{\mu}$$

Here, $(3/2)kT$ is the thermal energy of one molecule, while M/μ is the number of molecules in the gas, μ being the molecular mass.

Show that the above criterion can also be expressed as

$$M > 3.7 \left(\frac{k}{\mu} \frac{T}{G}\right)^{3/2} \frac{1}{\rho^{1/2}} \tag{4.17}$$

(The factor 3.7 was obtained from more accurate calculations.)

Problem 4.3: Star Formation

Initially, stars are formed through condensation of H-I clouds (clouds of neutral hydrogen), which have a density of about 100 atoms/cm^3 and a temperature $T \approx 100°$K. Estimate the minimal mass such a cloud must have in order to become unstable. Discuss the ramifications of this result to the theory of star formation (read the instructions to the solutions of the problems).

NONDEGENERATE STARS

For "normal" stars (i.e., those that lie on the main sequence of the Hertzsprung-Russel diagram) like our sun, we may approximate the equation of state quite accurately by that of an ideal gas:

$$pV = R_G T \tag{4.18}$$

where R_G is the gas constant. The mole volume V can be expressed in terms of the density ρ by

$$V = L\mu/\rho \qquad (4.19)$$

here $L = 6 \times 10^{23}$ is Avogadro's (also called Loschmidt's) number, and μ is the mass of one gas molecule. Normal stars contain mostly hydrogen, so for μ we shall use the value $\mu \approx 1.6 \times 10^{-27}$ kg. Equations (4.18) and (4.19) yield

$$\frac{p}{\rho} = \frac{R_G}{L} \frac{T}{\mu} = k \frac{T}{\mu} \qquad (4.20)$$

$k = R_G/L = 1.38 \times 10^{-23}$ J/K being Boltzmann's constant.

The equation of state of an ideal gas can now be written in the form we desire:

$$f(\rho,\ T) = \frac{p}{\rho c} = \frac{kT}{\mu c^2} = f(T) \qquad (4.21)$$

This result demonstrates that for an ideal gas the function $f(\rho,\ T)$ depends only on the temperature T. This function gives us the ratio of the mean kinetic energy (kT) to the rest energy (μc^2) of the gas molecules.

Thus, the ratio R/R, and hence the magnitude of relativistic effects, depends on the temperature T in the star's interior (to be consistent with our above approximation, we must use an average stellar temperature).

The interior stellar temperature is subject to the restriction that the light emitted by main sequence stars due to nuclear re-actions must continue to pour out at a steady and uniform rate. This occurs at temperatures of some 10^7 K. Consequently, $kT \approx 10^{-16}$ J $\approx 10^3$ eV = 1 keV, if we use the normal quantum-mechanical energy units (1 eV = 1.6×10^{-19} J). Now the energy equivalent of the mass of the hydrogen atom--the most abundant atom of stellar matter--has a value of $\mu c^2 \approx 1$ GeV, which implies that for *normal* stars

$$\frac{R}{R} \approx \frac{kT}{\mu c^2} \approx \frac{1 \text{ keV}}{1 \text{ GeV}} \approx 10^{-6}$$

(4.22)

Expressed in words, (4.22) says that for normal stars relativistic effects are of the order of 10^{-6}. This value can be traced directly to nuclear effects, which determine the temperatures and thus the pressure inside a star.

It is remarkable that the relativistic effects are independent of the gravitational constant.

THE EQUATION OF STATE OF DEGENERATE MATTER

In the previous section we have learned the following important fact: for normal stars that are located on the main sequence of the Hertzsprung-Russel diagram, and that burn their nuclear fuel uniformly and steadily, the ratio R/R is determined by the ratio of thermal energy to rest energy of the molecules. Due to the high temperatures in the stellar interior, we could safely neglect the particle interactions against the thermal energy, i.e., we could treat the stellar matter as an ideal gas. On the other hand, as the star approaches the end of its normal lifetime, having used up all its hydrogen fuel, it cannot maintain its high temperature any longer, thereby resulting in a decrease of its pressure.

As the star cools, its radius will swell, for according to (4.22)

$$R = R \frac{\mu c^2}{kT}$$

(4.23)

i.e., in order to maintain equilibrium radius and temperature will be inversely proportional to each other. The star grows to become a *red giant*, in whose core helium and heavier elements will maintain the nuclear reactions.

If the cooling continues, however, the star will eventually run out of the energy needed to reach new states of equilibrium, since this would require [according to (4.23)] further expansion against the gravitational pull.

The evolutionary phases of which we have just presented an overly simplified description are only a few of several highly complex processes that finally culminate in the star's contraction. In this phase the core reaches extremely high mean densities, a fact that allows the theory to become simpler again.

In order to find the equilibrium configurations of a star after it has run out of nuclear fuel we must again derive its equation of state. Since we are now dealing with very high densities, temperature variations of even millions of degrees do not affect the equation of state. We may thus set $T = 0$, and we see that in contrast to an ideal gas whose function f in Eq. (4.10) is a function of temperature alone, a very dense gas (star) is characterized by a function $f = f(\rho)$, which only depends on the density. Matter like this is called *degenerate*. Thus

$$f(\rho, \ T) = \frac{p}{\rho c^2} = \begin{cases} f(T) & \text{for an ideal gas} \\ f(\rho) & \text{for degenerate matter} \end{cases} \qquad (4.24)$$

For an ideal gas the pressure was determined by the kinetic molecular energy, while for a degenerate gas it is the kinetic energy of the electrons that is responsible for the pressure. Essentially any material, when submitted to several million atmospheres of pressure, will display metallic properties, and the electrons will behave like a free electron gas.

The high pressure of an electron gas is a result of Pauli's exclusion principle, which says that no two electrons can occupy the same quantum state. In a free electron gas one can characterize the different quantum states by the impulse of the electrons, or, equivalently, by the electron's position.

In order to distinguish the individual electrons by their position, their wave-functions must be concentrated in spatial cells of size d^3, d being the mean distance between two electrons (Fig. 4.6).

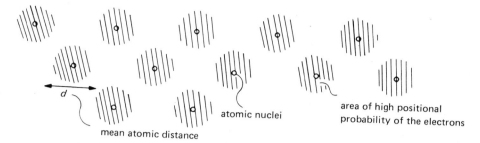

mean atomic distance   atomic nuclei   area of high positional probability of the electrons

Fig. 4.6. Distribution of electrons in a Fermi gas.

Restricting electrons to small areas of size d will provide them with an impulse p_F, which may be computed from Heisenberg's uncertainty relation

$$p_F d \approx \hbar \qquad (4.25)$$

Thus, the mutual restriction of electrons to small areas results in a mean impulse p_F and a mean kinetic energy

$$\varepsilon_F = p_F^2 / 2m \approx \hbar / md^2 \qquad (4.26)$$

We call ε_F the Fermi energy of the electron gas. The smaller the area that is available to an electron, the higher the resulting Fermi energy. In an electron gas of extremely high density it is not the temperature but the density that determines the kinetic energy of the electrons. Clearly, this happens if

$$\varepsilon_F \gg kT \qquad (4.27)$$

in which case the Fermi gas (electron gas) is called degenerate.

After this discussion we are ready to proceed with the derivation of the equation of state of a degenerate Fermi gas. neglecting precise numeric factors (as usual) we may substitute ε_F for the kinetic energy kT of the particles in an ideal gas:

$$\frac{p}{\rho c^2} \approx \frac{\varepsilon_F}{\mu c^2} \approx \frac{\hbar^2}{m \mu d^2 c^2} \qquad (4.28)$$

For a given mean particle distance d, the lightest particles will have the largest Fermi energy (since $\varepsilon_F \propto m^{-1}$), and hence contribute the most to the pressure. If we consider highly dense stellar matter, consisting of electrons and protons, then Eq. (4.26) tells us that the pressure of the proton gas is negligible when compared to the pressure of the electron gas. The electron mass m is the primary cause for the pressure, while the larger proton mass μ is the determining factor for the rest mass density of the gas. The density ρ as a function of the mean particle distance d is therefore given by

$$\rho \approx \frac{m + \mu}{d^3} \approx \frac{\mu}{d^3} \qquad (4.29)$$

Substituting (4.29) into (4.28) yields the equation of state of the degenerate Fermi gas:

$$\frac{p}{\rho c^2} \approx \frac{\hbar^2 \rho^{2/3}}{m \mu^{5/3} c^2} = \frac{m}{\mu}\left(\frac{\rho}{\rho_C}\right)^{2/3} \qquad (4.30)$$

Here,

$$\rho_C = \frac{\mu}{(\hbar/mc)^3} \qquad (4.31)$$

is that density at which the mean proton distance (and thus also the electron distance) has decreased down to the electron Compton wavelength $\lambda_e = \hbar/mc \approx 4 \times 10^{-13}$ m. Numerically, we have $\rho_C \approx 3 \times 10^{10}$ kg/m^3.

The equation of state given in formulation (4.30) has the advantage of underlining two important facts: first, the factor m/μ demonstrates that the pressure depends on the electrons (of mass m), while the rest mass density ρ is a result of the protons (of mass μ). Second, we see that at density ρ_C a radical change takes place: if we substitute the electron's mean distance $d \approx \lambda_e = \hbar/mc$ into Eq. (4.25), we find

$$p\hbar/mc \approx \hbar, \qquad \text{i.e.,} \qquad p \approx mc \qquad (4.32)$$

For $\rho = \rho_C$ the electrons move almost at the speed of light, requiring us to apply the relation between energy and impulse as
given by special relativity:[1]

$$\varepsilon_F \approx pc \qquad\qquad (4.33)$$

Using this equation in (4.28), a brief calculation yields

$$\frac{p}{\rho c^2} \approx \frac{m}{\mu}\left(\frac{\rho}{\rho_C}\right)^{1/3} \qquad \text{for} \quad \rho > \rho_C \qquad\qquad (4.34)$$

Summarizing our results so far, we find the equation of state
of degenerate matter to be

$$f(\rho) = \frac{p}{\rho c^2} \approx \frac{m}{\mu}\left(\frac{\rho}{\rho_C}\right)^{n/3} \qquad\qquad (4.35)$$

where $n = 2$ for $\rho < \rho_C \approx 3 \times 10^{10}$ kg/m^3 and $n = 1$ for $\rho > \rho_C$. [A
glance at Fig. 4.8 shows that Eq.(4.35) is in good agreement with
more accurate calculations in the regime 10^4 kg/m^3 $< \rho < 10^{13}$
kg/m^3.]

THE THEORY OF WHITE DWARFS

We shall now proceed to construct stellar models in the density range of 10^4 to 10^{13} kg/m^3. These will be the white dwarfs,
whose mass, density, and radius we shall compute. Our point of
departure is the chain of Eq.(4.17):

$$R/R \approx GM/Rc^2 \approx p/\rho c^2 = f(\rho) \qquad\qquad (4.36)$$

with $f(\rho)$ described by Eq.(4.35). Since $M \approx \rho R^3$, we obtain

[1]The following relation is only valid for extremely relativistic particles. However, we may apply it also for relativistic
electrons satisfying (4.32), since our treatment is only an
approximation to begin with.

$$f(\rho) \approx \frac{GM}{Rc^2} \approx \frac{GM}{c^2 (M/\rho)^{1/3}} \approx \frac{GM^{2/3} \rho^{1/3}}{c^2} \qquad (4.37)$$

or, after solving for M,

$$M(\rho) \approx \frac{f(\rho)^{3/2}}{\rho^{1/2}} \frac{c^3}{G^{3/2}} \qquad (4.38)$$

Substituting $f(\rho)$ according to Eq.(4.35) gives us the mass of white dwarfs as a function of their mean density ρ:

$$M(\rho) = \frac{1}{\rho^{1/2}} \left(\frac{m}{\mu}\right)^{3/2} (\rho/\rho_C)^{n/2} \frac{c^3}{G^{3/2}}$$

or

$$M(\rho) = \begin{cases} \left(\dfrac{mc^2}{G\mu}\right)^{3/2} \dfrac{\rho^{1/2}}{\rho_C} & \text{for} \quad \rho < \rho_C \\[4ex] \left(\dfrac{mc^2}{G\mu}\right)^{3/2} \dfrac{1}{\rho_C^{1/2}} & \text{for} \quad \rho > \rho_C \end{cases} \qquad (4.39)$$

In Fig. 4.7 we have compared this mass spectrum with the predictions from more accurate calculations.

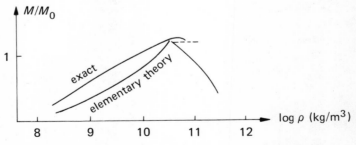

Fig. 4.7.   Mass-density curve for white dwarfs.

Examination of (4.39) reveals that for $\rho = \rho_C$ the mass $M(\rho)$ reaches a maximal value. This upper limit is known as the *Chandrasekhar limit* (or *Chandrasekhar mass*) M_C. Substituting Eq. (4.31) for ρ_C into (4.39) gives

$$M_C = \left(\frac{mc^2}{G\mu}\right)^{3/2} \frac{1}{\rho_C^{1/2}} = \left(\frac{mc^2}{G\mu}\right)^{3/2} \left(\frac{\hbar}{mc}\right)^{3/2} \frac{1}{\mu^{1/2}}$$

Thus

$$\text{Chandrasekhar limit } M_C = \left(\frac{\hbar c}{G\mu^2}\right)^{3/2} \mu \qquad (4.40)$$

Since both μ and M_C have the unit of a mass, the expression in parentheses in (4.40) must be dimensionless. Indeed,

$$\alpha_G = G\mu^2/\hbar c \approx 6 \times 10^{-39} \qquad (4.41)$$

is a dimensionless constant: the fine-structure constant of gravitation. α_G characterizes the strength of the gravitational interaction just as Sommerfeld's fine-structure constant

$$\alpha = e^2/4\pi\varepsilon_0\hbar c = 1/137$$

describes the strength of electromagnetic interactions (e is the electromagnetic elementary charge).

Using α_G from (4.41) in Eq.(4.40) gives us

$$M_C \approx \alpha_G^{-3/2}\mu \approx 2 \times 10^{57}\mu \approx 3 \times 10^{30} \text{ kg} \approx 1.5 M_\odot \qquad (4.42)$$

Equation (4.40) shows that $\hbar$ enters into the Chandrasekhar mass M_C. This leads to the following interesting observation:

Planck's quantum of action $\hbar$ not only determines the structure of elementary particles but also the mass scale and the inner structure of stars.

As a matter of fact, one could use Eq.(4.40) to find the order of magnitude of Planck's constant based on knowledge of the solar mass!

The results in this chapter have a tremendous impact on our perception of the universe since they demonstrate that the size of stars is not given at random. In fact, we are capable of deriving the structure of celestial objects (at least of white dwarfs) quite systematically from known physical laws. During our discussion of cosmogony in Chapter 10, we shall see to what generality such derivations are possible.

The radii of white dwarfs are obtained from

$$R \approx \left(\frac{M}{\rho}\right)^{1/3} = \left(\frac{M_C}{\rho_C}\right)^{1/3} \left(\frac{M}{M_C}\right)^{1/3} \left(\frac{\rho_C}{\rho}\right)^{1/3} \tag{4.43}$$

and the relation

$$M = M_C (\rho/\rho_C)^{1/2} \tag{4.44}$$

which follows from Eq.(4.39). If we denote the radius of the heaviest white dwarf (mass $= M_C$) by R_C, we find

$$R = R_C (\rho/\rho_C)^{1/6}, \qquad R_C = (M_C/\rho_C)^{1/3} \tag{4.45}$$

Using $M_C \approx \alpha_G^{-3/2} \mu$, $\rho_C \approx \mu \lambda_e^{-3}$, finally yields

$$R_C \approx \lambda_e \alpha_G^{-1/2} \approx 10^7 \text{ m} \tag{4.46}$$

Thus, the typical radius of white dwarfs is of the order of a few thousand kilometers.

Equations (4.44) and (4.45) lead to a further interesting relation:

$$MR^3 \approx M_C R_C^3 \tag{4.47}$$

The radii of white dwarfs decrease with increasing mass. Furthermore, relativistic effects for white dwarfs are given by

$$\delta \approx \frac{\Delta \nu}{\nu} \approx \frac{\Delta M}{M} \approx \frac{R}{R} \approx \frac{p}{\rho c^2} \approx f(\rho) \approx \frac{m}{\mu} \left(\frac{\rho}{\rho_C} \right)^{2/3} \approx 10^{-4} \qquad (4.48)$$

The red shift and the deflection of light around white dwarfs are primarily determined by the ratio of electron mass (m) to proton mass (μ). It is quite fascinating to watch this interaction of quantum mechanics, general relativity, and astrophysics.

The best known white dwarf is Sirius B, whose existence was postulated by Bessel in 1834 to explain the sinusoidal orbit of Sirius. Eighteen years later it was discovered by Clark. It is characterized by the following data:

Mass: $1.02 M_{\odot}$
Density: 3×10^9 kg/m^3
Radius: 5400 km
Red shift: 2.7×10^{-4}

Initially, astronomers believed that Sirius B was an ordinary star of very low luminosity. Spectroscopic measurements that were undertaken in 1914 revealed, however, that this star has the very high surface temperature of 24,000 K, thus emitting white light. As it turned out, the low luminosity was due to the small surface area, rather than a low temperature.

Subsequently, a large number of white dwarfs were discovered. Their frequency in our closer environment is estimated at about 0.001 white dwarfs per cubic light year, which corresponds to an average distance of 10 light years. In other words, white dwarfs are quite common in our galaxy.

MOONS, PLANETS, AND WHITE DWARFS

In the previous section we derived the upper mass limit M_C, or equivalently, the lower radius limit R_C, for white dwarfs. The next few pages are devoted to finding the lower mass limit M_p of white dwarfs, thereby drawing the border line between stars and planets.

As a first step we must improve the equation of state (4.35) in the lower density regime. In fact, Eq.(4.35) predicts that $\rho \to 0$ as $p \to 0$, contrary to the fact that even cold and pressure-less matter has a nonzero density. Of course, the particular value $\rho(p = 0) = \rho_0$ is dependent on the chemical structure of the material, but for planets, moons, and most terrestial objects a value of

$$\rho_0 \approx \mu/r_B^3 \approx 8000 \text{ kg/m}^3 \tag{4.49}$$

is typical. Here,

$$r_B = \frac{\lambda_e}{\alpha} = 0.5 \times 10^{-10} \text{ m} \tag{4.50}$$

is Bohr's radius ($\alpha = 1/137$ is Sommerfeld's fine-structure constant mentioned earlier, and $\lambda_e \approx 10^{-12}$ m is the Compton wave-length of the electron).

All those objects have one thing in common, namely, that their atomic structure is determined by electromagnetic interactions. The pressure due to gravity does not have any measurable effect on their quantum structure. However, if the mass, and consequently the pressure exceed a certain threshold, the atomic structure breaks down.

This threshold represents the border between planets and white dwarfs. In order to compute this value, we must improve the equation of state (4.35) as shown in Fig. 4.8.

For low pressures we approximate the density $\rho(p)$ by the constant $\rho(p) = \rho_0$, while for $p > p_0$ $\rho(p)$ is given by Eq.(4.35). The point of transition p_0 that marks the breakdown of the atomic structure is defined as the intersection of the straight line $\rho = \rho_0$ with the curve determined by (4.35).

Since $\rho = \rho_0$ for $p < p_0$, we find

$$M \approx \rho_0 R^3 \qquad \text{for} \qquad p < p_0 \tag{4.51}$$

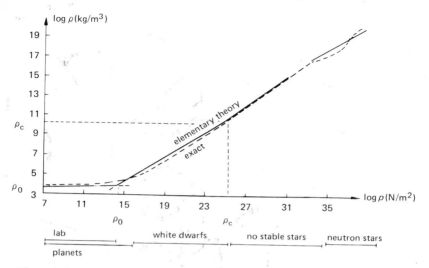

Fig. 4.8. Improved equation of state: for $p \leq p_0$ we set $\rho = \rho_0$; for $p > p_0$ we use Eq.(4.35) to compute ρ. Exact calculations (Harrison-Wheeler equation of state) show remarkable agreement with our "naive" theory!

On the other hand, for $p > p_0$ we have to apply Eq.(4.47):

$$MR^3 = M_C R_C^3 \qquad for \qquad p > p_0 \qquad\qquad (4.52)$$

To facilitate the determination of p_0, we graphically represent Eqs.(4.51) and (4.52) in a mass-radius diagram in Fig. 4.9. At the point of intersection of both curves, we find the maximal planetary mass M_p as well as the maximal planetary radius R_p. Alternatively, M_p can be interpreted as the lower mass limit of white dwarfs.

We obtain M_p by setting $\rho = \rho_0$ in the mass formula (4.44) for white dwarfs. Using Eqs.(4.49) and (4.50) leads to a numerical value for M_p:

$$M_p = M_C (\rho_0/\rho_C)^{1/2} \approx M_C \alpha^{3/2} \approx 2 \times 10^{27} \text{ kg} \qquad (4.53)$$

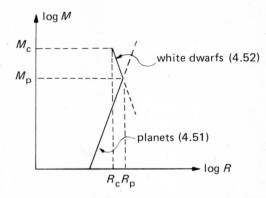

Fig. 4.9. Mass-radius curve for planets and white dwarfs.

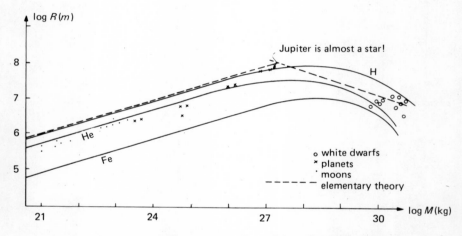

Fig. 4.10. Mass-radius curve for white dwarfs, planets, and
their moons according to Dehnen. The three theoretical curves
refer to objects consisting of hydrogen (H), helium (He), and iron
(Fe), respectively.

One of this chapter's key results may now be stated as follows:

White dwarfs can only exist in the narrow mass regime
given by

$$M_p \approx 2 \times 10^{27} \text{ kg} < M < M_C \approx 3 \times 10^{30} \text{ kg} \qquad (4.54)$$

On the other hand, the mass regime that corresponds to $\rho = \rho_0$ ($p < p_0$) is enormously large: it extends from the mass μ of a single hydrogen atom to the maximal planetary mass $M_p \approx 10^{54}$ $\mu \approx 2 \times 10^{27}$ kg.

The results of the simple-minded theory we have just developed are shown in Fig. 4.10 as a dotted curve.   This curve is compared to more sophisticated theoretical results (solid curves), which even take into account the chemical consistency of the objects under consideration.   Also included are the actual mass-radius positions of the moons and planets in the solar system, as well as of a few "neighboring" white dwarfs.   The agreement between theory and observation is quite remarkable!

Problem 4.4:   High-Pressure Physics

Compute the numerical value p_0 of the pressure at which the atomic structure breaks down.   Show that this pressure--in agreement with Fig. 4.8--lies about one order of magnitude above the pressures obtainable in lab experiments.   Is this a coincidence?

Problem 4.5:   Planetary Radii

Compute the maximal radius R_p for planets and white dwarfs. Compare the answer with the radius of Jupiter.

NEUTRON STARS

One of the most important developments of astronomy in recent years was the discovery of pulsars by Hewish and his colleagues in

1968 and the subsequent identification of pulsars with neutron stars.

Before entering into the discussion of this discovery, however, we would like to present the equally fascinating theoretical derivation of the properties of neutron stars, this derivation being due to Landau (1932) and Oppenheimer and Volkoff (1939).

To begin with, we shall extend the equation of state (4.35) to the density region 10^{13} kg/m^3 < ρ < 10^{20} kg/m^3. Characteristic for this density regime is an increase in the Fermi energy of the electrons to a point at which inverse β decay takes place:

$$e + p \rightarrow n + \nu_e \qquad\qquad (4.55)$$

where e is an electron, p a proton, n a neutron, and ν_e a neutrino.

The neutrons are heavier than the protons by 1 MeV (about two electron masses), yet the above reaction produces energy, since the disappearance of the electron results in the loss of the Fermi energy ε_F.[2] With increasing density more and more neutrons are produced and generate heavy neutron-rich atomic nuclei.

The decrease in the number of electrons caused by the inverse β decay is responsible for the fact that the pressure will not rise but will fall with increasing density, contrary to Eq. (4.35). This in turn leads to the sudden drop of the equilibrium mass $M(\rho)$ with increasing density ρ shown in Fig. 4.7.

As ρ exceeds 10^{16} kg/m^3, the individual atomic nuclei fall apart and uniform neutron matter is the result! Now the neutrons take over the role of the electrons: with rising density, their Fermi energy increases, and again the pressure rises.

[2]*Analogous reasons prevent the decay of neutrons in the atomic nucleus: the arising proton would occupy such an unfavorable energy state in the nucleus that the decay simply does not occur.*

In order to obtain the function $f(\rho)$ in this density regime, we simply substitute the neutron mass for the electron mass m in all the relevant equations. The neutron mass, however, is roughly equal to the proton mass μ and so we replace m by μ in all equations. Equation of state (4.35) now becomes

$$f(\rho) = p/\rho c^2 \approx (\rho/\rho_1)^{n/3}$$

where

$$n = \begin{cases} 2 & \text{for} \quad \rho < \rho_1 \\ 1 & \text{for} \quad \rho > \rho_1 \end{cases} \qquad (4.56)$$

$$\rho_1 = \frac{\mu}{(\hbar/\mu c)^3} \approx 10^{20} \text{ kg/m}^3 \qquad (4.57)$$

Here ρ_1 is that density at which the neutrons reach relativistic speed $v \approx c$ due to their Fermi energy. If we substitute $m \to \mu$ in Eq. (4.39), we obtain

$$M(\rho) = \begin{cases} \left(\dfrac{c^2}{G}\right)^{3/2} \dfrac{\rho^{1/2}}{\rho_1} = M_C \left(\dfrac{\rho}{\rho_1}\right)^{1/2} & \text{for} \quad \rho < \rho_1 \\ M_C & \text{for} \quad \rho > \rho_1 \end{cases} \qquad (4.58)$$

This shows that the upper mass limit for neutron stars (which is reached for $\rho = \rho_1$) is identical to that for white dwarfs since m does not appear in the Chandrasekhar limit (4.40).

The entire mass spectrum of degenerate stars is depicted in Fig. 4.11. This figure shows the results of our elementary model vs. those of more accurate computations. The three curves reflect different models of matter under extreme pressures. The discrepancy in their shapes arises from the difficulty of theoretically treating the "strong interaction" among elementary particles in the nuclear matter. When compared to curves a, b, c, we see that even our naive approximations reflect the shape of the curve $M(\rho)$ at least qualitatively.

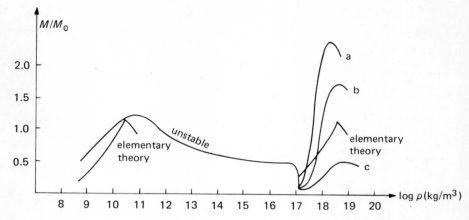

Fig. 4.11. Mass spectrum of degenerate stars, comparison between elementary theory and exact calculations.

The following (simplified) argument should make it plausible that there are no stable stars in the density region $10^{11} < \rho < 10^{16}$ kg/m^3. Suppose that a star in this region begins to oscillate and contracts slightly (so that $\rho \rightarrow \rho + \delta\rho$). According to Fig. 4.12, a star with density $\rho + \delta\rho$ must have a *smaller* mass $M(\rho + \delta\rho) < M(\rho)$ to be stable [i.e., *less* gravitational pull is needed to balance the interior pressure $P(\rho + \delta\rho)$]. Due to the higher mass $M(\rho)$, i.e., higher gravitational force, our star will contract further, instead of returning to its original size. Similarly, if a star in that density region expands (so $\rho \rightarrow \rho - \delta\rho$), it will take a *larger* mass $M(\rho - \delta\rho) > M(\rho)$ to counteract the interior pressure. Thus, the star will continue to expand, again becoming unstable. On the other hand, should a white dwarf or neutron star contract ($\rho \rightarrow \rho + \delta\rho$), then it requires a larger mass (i.e., gravitational force) to balance the interior pressure. Since the star's mass $M(\rho)$ is too small, it will expand, thus returning to its initial size. Should the star expand ($\rho \rightarrow \rho - \delta\rho$), then a *smaller* mass (i.e., gravitational force) would balance the interior pressure. The excessive mass $M(\rho) > M(\rho - \delta\rho)$ will therefore cause a contraction back to its initial size.

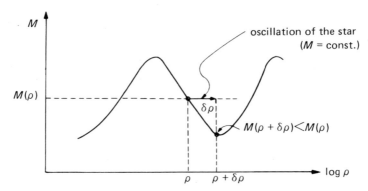

Fig. 4.12. The regime of decrease of the equilibrium curve does not tolerate stable stars!

We can obtain the radii of neutron stars by simply replacing λ_e by the Compton wavelength for neutrons $\lambda_n \approx 10^{-16}$ m in Eqs. (4.46) and (4.47). Thus, we find

$$MR^3 \approx M_C R_n^3 \qquad\qquad (4.59)$$

and

$$R_n \approx \lambda_n \alpha_G^{-1/2} \approx 10 \text{ km} \qquad\qquad (4.60)$$

Neutron stars are objects with a radius of a few kilometers but with masses comparable to the sun.

From Eqs.(4.56) and (4.17) we can deduce the ratio of Schwarzschild radius to neutron star radius, i.e., the order of magnitude of the relativistic effects near neutron stars:

$$\delta \approx \frac{\Delta\nu}{\nu} \approx \frac{\Delta M}{M} \approx \frac{R}{R} \approx \frac{p}{\rho c^2} = f(\rho) \approx \left(\frac{\rho}{\rho_1}\right)^{2/3} \approx 1 \qquad (4.61)$$

For normal (main sequence) stars R/R is essentially determined by the ratio of the energy level distances in the atomic nucleus, which is a very small parameter. For white dwarfs, it is the small ratio of electron to proton mass, which causes relativistic effects to be still insignificant. The difference for neutron

stars is that there appears no such parameter. Thus, another key
result of this chapter is

For neutron stars the relativistic effects are of the
order 1.

COSMIC STRUCTURES

The results of this chapter can be displayed in a transparent
diagram that gives an overview of the multitude of structures that
we find in the cosmos. This chapter dealt with those structures
that are listed as "quantum-mechanically stabilized" in Fig. 4.13.
They are characterized by the fact that they remain stable without
any rotation and even at temperatures T near absolute zero.

In contrast, the dotted main sequence stars and giants are
thermally stabilized, i.e., they are only stable as long as they
maintain their interior temperature. Figure 4.13 raises an important question: for degenerate stars (white dwarfs and neutron
stars) the Chandrasekhar limit M_C is an upper mass limit as well
as a characteristic size. Why do we find normal stars in the same
mass region $M \approx M_C$? In particular, is $\hbar$ essential for the calculation of M_C? What is the role of $\hbar$ in the structure of normal
stars? These questions will be dealt with in Problem 4.6.

The shaded structures in Fig. 4.13 maintain their stability
due to the kinetic energy of the stars (planets) that they contain. Typical representatives of these structures are solar
systems, globular clusters, and galaxies.

The following chain of equations must be supplemented to Fig.
4.13:

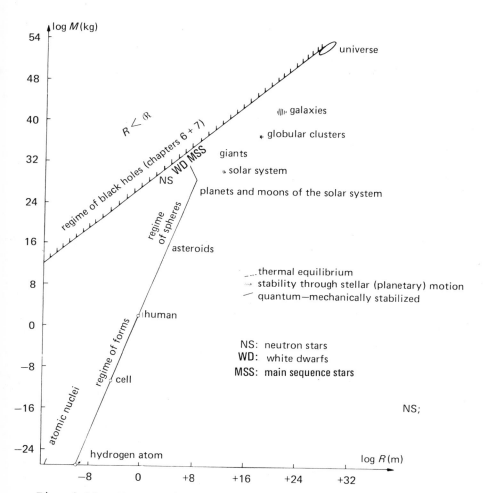

Fig. 4.13. *Mass-radius diagram of the cosmic structures.*

$$\delta \approx \frac{\Delta \nu}{\nu} \approx \frac{\Delta M}{M} \approx \frac{R}{R} \approx \frac{p}{\rho c^2}$$

$$= f(\rho, T) = \begin{cases} \dfrac{kT}{\mu c^2} \approx 10^{-6} & \text{(MSS)} \\[3ex] \dfrac{m}{\mu} \left(\dfrac{\rho}{\rho_0}\right)^{2/3} \approx 10^{-4} & \text{(WD)} \\[3ex] \left(\dfrac{\rho}{\rho_1}\right)^{2/3} \approx 1 & \text{(NS)} \end{cases} \qquad (4.62)$$

where MSS are main sequence stars, WD white dwarfs, and NS neutron stars.

Figure 4.13 suggests the following fundamental questions of cosmogony:

Why do we find precisely these structures in the cosmos? How did these structures evolve? With which frequency do these structures occur? Are there any other structures in the universe?

The first question has been answered at least partially in this chapter. We were able to theoretically determine the masses of those structures that are quantum mechanically and thermally stabilized.

The understanding of structures that are stable due to rotation is a problem of much higher complexity. Today we have barely begun to explain solar systems, galaxies, and stellar clusters. We shall deal with this subject matter again in Chapter 10, where we shall try to sketch the current research into the basic questions of cosmogony, and the immense problems that are being faced.

Problem 4.6: The Mass of Main Sequence Stars

We have seen that degenerate stars within the mass regime $10^{-3} M_\odot \leq M \leq 2 M_\odot$ are stable. Here the solar mass $M_\odot$ as a characteristic unit is essentially determined by $\hbar$. An interesting fact is that there exists a similar region of stability for (nondegen-erate) main sequence stars, namely $10^{-2}M_\odot \leq M \leq 60M_\odot$. The lower limit is given by the minimal size necessary for the onset of nuclear reactions. The upper limit, on the other hand, is derived from the fact that the radiation pressure

$$p_R \approx (kT)^4/(\hbar c)^3$$

exceeds the interior gas pressure, thus resulting in instabilities. Show that the condition $p_R < p$ leads to $M < M_\odot$ if numerical factors are neglected (the correct inequality would be $M \leq 100M_\odot$).

Problem 4.7: Planets and Moons

Planets and moons differ from smaller objects in that their binding energy E_B is determined by gravity rather than by solid-state effects (like, e.g., meteors). Show that this is the case for masses M, satisfying

$$M > M_m \approx M_P\left(\frac{\varepsilon}{A}\,\alpha^2 mc^2\right)^{3/2} \approx 10^{-5}M_P \approx 10^{22} \text{ kg}$$

where $\varepsilon \approx 1$ eV is the binding energy per atom due to solid-state effects, and $A \approx 50$ is the mass number of the atoms. M_m is the *minimal* mass of a planet or moon (compare the next problem).

Problem 4.8: Forms and Spheres

In contrast to our moon, which is almost spherical, the moon Phobos that orbits Mars deviates considerably from a sphere (see Fig. 4.14). The reason can be found in the higher mass of our moon: masses that exceed a certain limiting mass cannot develop major deviations from a spherical geometry since their gravita-tional field is large. We shall estimate this effect by calcu-lating the maximal possible altitude of mountains that can exist on a planet (see Fig. 4.15).

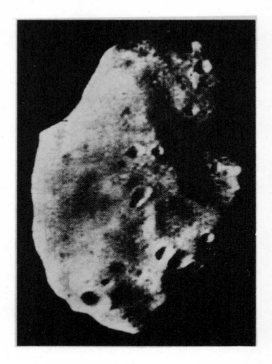

Fig. 4.14.   The Martian moon Phobos, photographed in 1971 by
Mariner 9.   The moon shows a clear deviation from a spherical
shape.

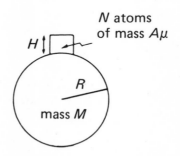

Fig. 4.15.   The height of mountains.

The formation of a mountain of height H and mass m requires a potential energy of roughly $E \approx mgH = N\mu AHg$. Here g is the local gravitational acceleration, and N the number of atoms, each with mass $A\mu$ (see Fig. 4.15). This mountain is stable, if its binding energy $E_B \approx N\epsilon$ exceeds the potential energy E, i.e., if

$$E_B \approx N\epsilon > N\mu AHMG/R^2$$

Show that this condition leads to

$$\frac{H}{R} < \left(\frac{M_m}{M}\right)^{2/3} = \left(\frac{R_m}{R}\right)^2$$

Objects with $M \gg M_m$ will therefore show no significant deviation from a sphere.

CHAPTER 5

PULSARS

THE DISCOVERY OF PULSARS

In the summer of 1967 the brand new radio telescope at
Cambridge began to operate. It was intended to study scintilla-
tions of signals from radio galaxies, which are caused by clouds
of plasma in the solar wind. The anticipated effects were fluctuations in the radio signal, occurring randomly, and typically
lasting for fractions of seconds.

As the year 1967 went by, the radio telescope received a
highly regular signal, which came from a certain area of the
galaxy, and lasted for about 20 msec during every second.

Now, signals of a duration of $\tau = 2 \times 10^{-2}$ sec can only be
emitted from objects that are smaller than $R \leq c\tau = 3 \times 10^{8} \times 2 \times$
10^{-2} m $= 6 \times 10^{6}$ m $= 6000$ km. Consequently, astronomers first
thought of planets and unknown civilizations trying to make contact with us. Thus, the first four pulsars were labeled LGM1, 2,
3, and 4 by the Cambridge astronomers, LGM meaning "little green
men." (For some reason, inhabitants of other planets are always
thought to be green!)

Figure 5.1 shows the complex form of the radio pulses origi-
nating from a pulsar, which could easily convey the idea of an
intelligent source. Closer analysis of these signals, however,
revealed such an enormous output of energy that the theory of mes-
sages from a civilization could no longer be maintained. Instead,
two major questions arose, concerning the explanation of these
mysterious signals:

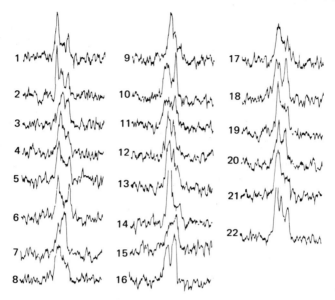

Fig. 5.1.   Sequence of contiguous pulses from CP1919.

Fundamental problems of the physics of pulsars: (1) What kind of objects are capable of emitting the observed signals?   (2) What mechanism causes the emission of this enormous amount of radiation?

The first question has been answered by astronomers, who seem to agree that pulsars must be neutron stars. The second question, however, is still far from being answered satisfactorily.

The principal argument in favor of the theory that pulsars are neutron stars is based on the shortness of the pulsars' signal periods, the smallest of which has been measured in the Crab nebula (NP 0532) to $\tau = 0.033$ sec. Assuming that the periodicity of the signals is a result of the pulsar's rotation, we know that the surface velocity of the pulsar cannot exceed the speed of light. Thus, if R is the pulsar's radius, we find that $2\pi R/\tau < c$, which yields a radius

$$R < \frac{\tau c}{2\pi} < \frac{3 \times 10^{-2} \times 3 \times 10^{8}}{2\pi} \text{ m} \approx 700 \text{ km} \tag{5.1}$$

An object of that size that produces intensive electromagnetic
radiation (thereby eliminating planets) can only be a neutron
star.

Another fact that supports this theory is the high regularity
of the temporal sequence with which the pulses are emitted. This
regularity is shown in Table 5.1, where the periods P of a few
pulses have been listed with ten digits of accuracy. Such precise
signals can only originate from extremely rigid objects. The last
column in Table 5.1 reveals a remarkable phenomenon: the pulsar
periods show a slow increase with time, i.e., $\dot{P} = dP/dt > 0$.

If we explain the pulses as caused by the rotation of the object, then $\dot{P} > 0$ means a slowdown of that rotation with time, and
we can define a characteristic time

$$t = P/\dot{P} \tag{5.2}$$

For the first four pulsars listed in Table 5.1, we find $t \approx 10^{14}$
sec $\approx 10^7$ years. On the other hand, for the Crab pulsar NP 0532,
$t \approx 10^{11}$ sec ≈ 3000 years. In other words, it appears that *the
Crab pulsar has changed significantly within a historic time
frame.* Indeed, astronomers have linked this pulsar with the
supernova observed by the Chinese in the year 1054 A.D. A supernova occurs when a normal star of a few solar masses runs out of

TABLE 5.1. Pulsar Parameters.[a]

	Period P (sec)	$\dot{P}$ $(10^{-15}$ sec/sec)
CP 0834	1.2737631515	5.0 ± 0.8
CP 0950	0.2530650372	0.3 ± 0.1
CP 1133	1.1879109795	4.1 ± 0.5
CP 1919	1.337301109	1.1 ± 0.5
NP 0532	0.03309114	350

[a]*The periods are with respect to the center of gravity of the
solar system.*

its nuclear fuel, resulting in a sudden loss of interior pressure and temperature. The star collapses rapidly, tremendous shock waves travel outwards, and part of the star's mass is pushed off in a vast explosion (this mass then forms a nebula around the supernova). The remaining part of the star becomes a neutron star.

There are two points of particular importance for the collapse phase: first, the angular momentum of the star

$$L \approx MR^2 \omega \tag{5.3}$$

is conserved during the collapse. Here M is the star's mass, R its radius, and ω the angular velocity of the rotating star. For our sun, these quantities are

$$M \approx 2 \times 10^{30} \text{ kg}$$

$$R \approx 7 \times 10^8 \text{ m} \tag{5.4}$$

$$\omega \approx 3 \times 10^{-6} \text{ sec}^{-1}$$

The conservation of the angular momentum implies $R^2\omega = \text{const.}$ Thus, the formation of a neutron star of radius $R_1 \approx 5 \times 10^4$ m requires an angular velocity of $\omega_1 \approx 10^4 \text{ sec}^{-1}$. In other words, an initially slowly rotating star will start to spin rapidly during its collapse. This then would explain the short periods that have been observed from pulsars.

The second point concerns the enormous increase of the star's rotational energy

$$E_{rot} \approx MR^2 \omega^2 \tag{5.5}$$

during the collapse. Substituting data for a typical star like our sun into Eq.(5.5) yields an energy of

$$E_{rot} \approx 10^{37} \text{ J} \tag{5.6}$$

for a normal star. For the neutron star that forms after the collapse, we must substitute R_1 and ω_1, resulting in an energy of

$$E_{rot} \approx 10^{45} \text{ J} \tag{5.7}$$

for the neutron star. This rotational energy is therefore comparable to the entire energy that a normal star (in the course of billions of years) produces due to nuclear fusion.

As a result of this discussion, we can conjecture that the slow decrease of the rotational velocity of the neutron star (pulsar) in the center of the Crab nebula supplies the entire energy for the nebula. Since we know the rate of slowdown ($\dot{P}$) of the pulsar period, i.e., the decrease of the star's rotation, we can compute the loss of rotational energy per second of the Crab pulsar. This energy loss agrees (to within an order of magnitude) with the total emitted energy of the Crab nebula, thus confirming the conjecture that this nebula is the result of a supernova explosion and the formation of a neutron star.

Problem 5.1: Rotation

When we estimated the maximal frequency with which a rigid object can rotate, we used the condition that the surface velocity cannot exceed the speed of light [Eq. (5.1)]. Actually, a much more severe restriction results from the condition that

$$v^2 \leq MG/R \tag{5.8}$$

since otherwise parts of the star's matter would be torn off the surface due to the centrifugal force. Show that this condition can be rewritten as

$$v^2/c^2 \leq R/R \tag{5.9}$$

or

$$\tau_{rot} \approx R/v > (G\rho)^{-1/2} \tag{5.10}$$

What lower limit for the rotational frequency of white dwarfs is obtained from (5.10)?

For which objects in Fig. 4.13 is condition (5.10) applicable? Why not for all objects?

Problem 5.2: Sound Speed and Pulsation

Fluctuations in the luminosity of many variable stars are not caused by rotation but by a pulsation of the stars. Here we address the problem of explaining pulsars through rapid expansion and contraction of white dwarfs. In order to estimate the duration of pulsation of a star we must first find the speed of sound in stellar matter. Show that the speed of sound

$$v_S^2 = \partial p/\partial \rho \tag{5.11}$$

can be approximated by

$$v_S^2/c^2 \approx \frac{R}{R} \tag{5.12}$$

and that v_S is of the same order of magnitude as the highest possible rotational speed of the object. Since a star's pulsation is an oscillation that travels with the speed of sound in the star's interior, we obtain for the pulsation frequency

$$\tau \approx R/v_S \approx (G\rho)^{-1/2} \tag{5.13}$$

In other words, this frequency is comparable to the rotational frequency τ_{rot}. We must therefore rule out the possiblity that pulsars are pulsating white dwarfs. However, there is yet another possibility, namely, that pulsars are pulsating (as the name would suggest) rather than rotating neutron stars. So far it has been impossible to explain the intense electromagnetic radiation of pulsars in this manner.

Problem 5.3: Variable Stars

The relationship $\tau \propto \rho^{-1/2}$ between pulsation frequency and mean density has actually been observed for many variable stars. If we let $\rho_{\odot} = 1400$ kg/m^3 be the mean density of our sun, we can write

$$\tau = b(\rho_{\odot}/\rho)^{1/2} \tag{5.14}$$

The constant b has been measured experimentally for the most important classes of variable stars:

Star	b (days)
Cδ, Cepheids	0.041
CW, Cepheids	0.160
RR, Lyrae stars	0.145
β, Can Maj-stars	0.027

Compare these values with the theoretical relation (5.13)!

MAGNETIC FIELD AND THE RADIATION MECHANISM

Rotational energy and angular velocity of a star are not the only quantities that change in a characteristic manner during collapse. Due to the conservation of the magnetic flux

$$BR^2 = \text{const} \tag{5.15}$$

there will be an increase of the magnetic field to about 10^8 times the original value during the formation of a neutron star. The magnetic field (magnetic induction) around pulsars is expected to reach intensities up to

$$B \approx 10^8 \text{ Tesla} \tag{5.16}$$

The physical processes that take place in such intense magnetic fields are largely unknown today. Consequently, we can only provide very general statements about the mechanism with which pulsars emit radiation. Most pulsar models are based on the

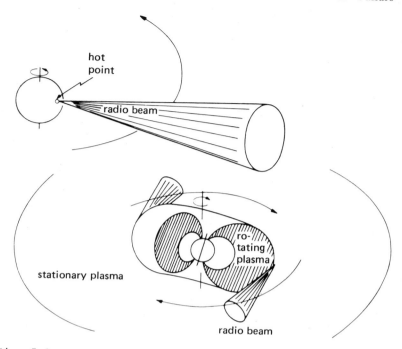

Fig. 5.2.   Two models of the mechanism of pulsar radiation.

postulate that the axis of the magnetic dipole field is nearly perpendicular to the pulsar's axis of rotation. The dipole field that rotates with the star becomes the source of an intense electromagnetic wave, which is emitted with the star's rotational frequency. This emission of radiation leads to a slowdown of the pulsar. It is probable that the emitted electromagnetic wave also provides the energy that makes the nebula surrounding the pulsar shine.

The pulsar mechanism itself, i.e., the star's emission of regular signals, can probably be imagined by comparing the two rotating magnetic poles of the pulsars to the two rotating lights of a light house. While they rotate they emit a light cone that extends from one or both poles and reaches the earth. Currently there is much debate over the question how close to the pulsar this radiation is actually produced (Fig. 5.2).

CHAPTER 6

GRAVITATIONAL COLLAPSE AND BLACK HOLES

In Chapter 4 we considered the equilibrium configurations of
matter, and became acquainted with two kinds of degenerate stars
that differ considerably from the "normal" main sequence stars.
We found that both types of degenerate stars can only exist up to
a maximal mass: the Chandrasekhar mass. What happens, though, if
a star with even higher mass reaches the end of its thermonuclear
burning phase? In this case no equilibrium configuration with
finite density exists, and the star will continue to collapse to a
"singularity," which is surrounded by a "black hole." This process will be the subject of the present chapter.

GRAVITATIONAL COLLAPSE

We know that stars maintain their equilibrium state due to
their interior pressure (counteracting the gravitational field).
On the other hand, it is not at all obvious why a structure like
our galaxy does not collapse. The individual stars that comprise
the galaxy are so remote from each other that they do not exert
any measurable pressure on one another.

Of course, it is possible that a hypothetical collapse of the
galaxy lasts so long that it does not lead to any observable
effects during the lifetime of the universe. In order to eliminate this possibility we shall compute the duration of the free
collapse of an object of constant density ρ. We assume that for
$t < 0$, the object (star, galaxy, etc.) is in equilibrium due to
interior pressure. At $t = 0$ this pressure suddenly drops to 0

(this is a very simplified model of a star that runs out of nuclear fuel). Thus, starting at $t = 0$, the object will collapse in
a free fall.

The equation of motion of a randomly picked atom on the surface of the collapsing mass is

$$m \frac{d^2 R}{dt^2} = - \frac{MG}{R^2} m \tag{6.1}$$

Here $M = (4\pi/3)\rho R^3$ = const is the total mass of the (spherical)
object, while m is the mass of the atom. Canceling m, multiplying
by dR/dt yields the conservation of energy law:

$$\frac{d}{dt}\left[\frac{1}{2}\left(\frac{dR}{dt} \right)^2 - \frac{MG}{R} \right] = 0 \tag{6.2}$$

or

$$\frac{1}{2}\left(\frac{dR}{dt} \right)^2 - \frac{MG}{R} = \text{const} = - \frac{MG}{R_0} \tag{6.3}$$

The constant R_0, which is defined by Eq. (6.3), is the initial
radius of the object (at $t \le 0$) since for $R = R_0$ we obtain dR/dt
$= 0$ from Eq. (6.3).

The differential Eq. (6.3) can be integrated easily:

$$t - t_0 = \int dt = \int \frac{dR}{[2GM(1/R - 1/R_0)]^{1/2}} \tag{6.4}$$

This integral can be found in every table of integrals:

$$t(R) = \left(\frac{RR_0(R_0 - R)}{2MG} \right)^{1/2}$$

$$+ R_0\left(\frac{R_0}{8MG} \right)^{1/2} \text{arc cos}\left(\frac{2R}{R_0} - 1 \right) \tag{6.5}$$

With this equation we have determined (at least implicitly) the
radius R of the collapsing object as a function of time t. The

constant of integration t_0 in Eq.(6.4) has been chosen so that the collapse starts at $t = 0$, i.e., $t(R_0) = 0$.

In order to find the time t_{coll} during which an object collapses (in free fall) to a point, we set $R = 0$ in Eq.(6.5):

$$t_{coll} = \pi \left(R_0^3 / 8MG \right)^{1/2} \approx (G\rho)^{-1/2} \qquad (6.6)$$

Note that the collapse time t_{coll} only depends on the mean density ρ, but not on the radius of the object.

With Eq.(6.6) we have found another interpretation of the time $T \approx (G\rho)^{-1/2}$, which was mentioned repeatedly in Chapter 5. In Fig. 6.1 we have listed several physical situations for which the time $T \approx (G\rho)^{-1/2}$ becomes relevant (compare also the problems at the end of this section).

 A Shortest rotational time t_{rot} of a stable object (for $t_{rot} < T$ matter will begin to lift from the surface). Compare Problem 5.1.

 B Pulsation frequency of a stable star (primary frequency). Compare Problem 5.2.

 C Orbit time of a satellite moving along the star's surface.

 D Collapse time t_{coll} of a nonrotating object that is not stabilized through interior pressure.

 E An object that is not stabilized through interior pressure must have this rotational frequency in order to avoid gravitational collapse. Compare Problem 5.4.

\\\\ Matter that is stabilized through interior pressure (e.g., solid object).

Matter with no interior pressure (e.g., galaxy).

Fig. 6.1. Relevance of $T = (G\rho)^{-1/2}$.

The last situation in Fig. 6.1 provides the explanation for the stability of the galaxy. For an object that is not stabilized through interior pressure (like the galaxy), the quantity $1/T \approx (G\rho)^{1/2}$ can be interpreted as the frequency with which the object must rotate in order to avoid gravitational collapse (see Problem 6.1).

The relevant data for our own galaxy are

$$M \approx 10^{11} \, M_{\odot} \approx 10^{41} \text{ kg}, \qquad R \approx 3 \times 10^{20} \text{ m} \qquad (6.7)$$

so that $\rho \approx 10^{-20}$ kg/m^3, and hence

$$t_{coll} \approx T \approx (G\rho)^{-1/2} \approx 10^{15} \text{ sec} \approx 100 \text{ million years} \qquad (6.8)$$

Without rotation, our galaxy would collapse in a matter of 10^8 years. Thus, we find that the rotation of the galaxy (which was postulated for the first time by I. Kant in his *General History of Nature and Theory of the Sky*) is a necessity for its existence. The rotational duration, which according to astronomical observations can be estimated at $t_R \approx 200$ million years, may also be approximated from Eq.(6.7). This is discussed further in Problem 6.2.

After these preliminary remarks we turn our attention to the collapse of stars. What happens after a normal star has exhausted its nuclear fuel, thus having reached the end of its thermonuclear evolutionary phase? Clearly, the star will no longer be able to maintain its interior temperature and pressure. Instead, it enters a complicated "aging" phase, which we can discuss using a highly simplified model.

Let us assume that the star runs out of energy instantaneously, causing pressure and temperature suddenly to drop to 0. The star that had so far been stable will now collapse in free fall. From Eq.(6.7) we can estimate the collapse time for a star of density $\rho \approx 10^3$ kg/m^3 (density of the sun):

$$t_{coll} \approx (G\rho)^{-1/2} \approx 3 \times 10^3 \text{ sec} \approx 1 \text{ hour} \qquad (6.9)$$

How far does the collapse go? Can there be a new equilibrium
configuration or does the star collapse to a point?

Stable degenerate stars, i.e., stars whose stability is governed by quantum effects rather than thermal pressure, can exist
up to the Chandrasekhar mass $M_C \approx 1.5 M_\odot$. Our discussion in
Chapter 4, however, has shown that this upper limit is theoretically vague, and for neutron stars it might be as large as $3 M_\odot$.

A collapsing star with mass $M < M_C$ will reach a new equilibrium state: as a white dwarf it will end its life by slowly
cooling off.

For stars with $M > M_C$, the collapse does not reach an equilibrium state that easily. According to theory (precise calculations
are very hard), it is probable that for $M \leq 10 M_\odot$ the collapse is
accompanied by tremendous shock waves that traverse the star and
possibly cause sufficient mass to be expelled to allow the remnant
mass to form a *neutron star*. This is probably the event that
takes place during a *supernova explosion*. The expelled mass of
gas will surround the star as a nebula. The best-known example is
the Crab nebula, which we discussed in Chapter 5.

Problem 6.1: Rotation

Estimate how fast an object without internal pressure must
rotate in order to remain stable against its gravitational force.
What must be the object's shape? How do the rotational time t_R
and rotational speed v depend on the distance from the center?

Problem 6.2: Rotation of the Galaxy

Figure 6.2 shows the rotational speed of our galaxy as a function of the distance from the galactic center. How is this curve
to be explained? Does Fig. 6.2 allow us to determine the mass of
the galaxy? How can this curve be obtained experimentally?

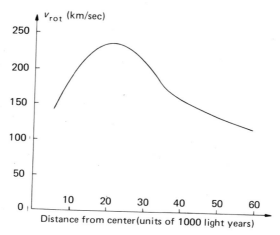

Fig. 6.2. Rotational velocity of our galaxy as a function of the distance from the galactic center.

BLACK HOLES

Stars with $M \lesssim 10M_\odot$ whose nuclear fuel has been used up will collapse until they (probably) reach a new stable configuration, that of a white dwarf or a neutron star. On the other hand, for $M \gtrsim 10M_\odot$ neither the electron pressure nor the neutron pressure will suffice to halt the star's collapse. In this case, Newton's gravitational theory predicts that the star will collapse to a point of infinite density, i.e., to a *singularity*.

Surprisingly, general relativity confirms Newton's prediction, but adds an essential supplement. The relativistic description of the collapse can best be studied by discussing Fig. 6.3, which is a very useful summary of the evolution and properties of *black holes*.

Figure 6.3 presents the gravitational collapse in a space-time diagram, following the collapse and the development of a black hole (from bottom to top). Shown is the collapse of a circular cross section through the star's center, i.e., of a disk of infinitesimal thickness.

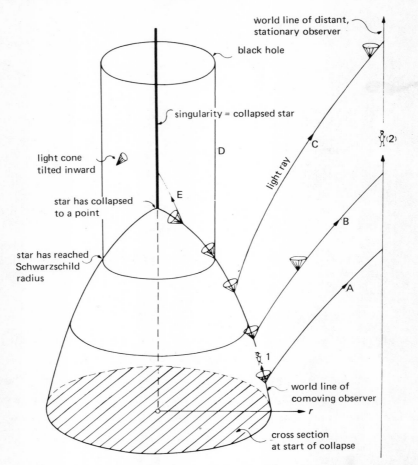

Fig. 6.3. Space-time diagram of a collapsing star = development of a black hole.

The vertical line in the center of Fig. 6.3 is the world line of the star's center. As we move upwards (i.e., forward in time) we see that the world line is surrounded by circles of ever decreasing radii. These are the cross-sectional disks that collapse with time, and finally at

$$t_{coll} \approx (G\rho)^{-1/2} \tag{6.10}$$

they converge to a point in agreement with both Newton's theory and Einstein's general relativity theory. In other words, at time t_{coll} the star becomes a singularity of infinite density. This singularity persists indefinitely (central thick line).

We know from general relativity that time intervals depend upon how far a clock is located from heavy masses. For which clocks therefore does the collapse last for the time t_{coll}? General relativity says that the time interval t_{coll} is measured by an observer (1) who sits on the star's surface and takes part in the collapse. For him, the time from the beginning of the collapse until its end as a singularity is precisely t_{coll} as given in (6.10).

For an observer who stays at a "safe" distance from the star, the situation is considerably different. The vertical line at the right-hand edge of Fig. 6.3 represents the world line of an observer (2) who watches the catastrophic end of the star at a safe and constant distance. In order to describe this observer's impressions we have to investigate the behavior of light rays in the neighborhood of the collapsing mass. This can be facilitated by drawing the light cones of a point on the star's surface at a few selected times during the collapse. Recall that the light cone is the set of all light rays (in the space-time diagram) that emanate from that point.

At a sufficiently large distance from the star the light cone is described simply by $|x| = ct$, i.e., it is a vertical cone that is open at the top. The cone is vertical since there is no gravitational field that can deflect light. Within the gravitational field of the star, however, the light cone is tilted toward the star's center since light tends to fall inwards due to gravity. Once a point falls inside the Schwarzschild radius the inward angle of its light cone becomes so extreme that no light can escape outwards.

We now assume that observer (1) intends to communicate with observer (2) during the collapse. Observer (1) will therefore

send light signals at constant intervals--measured in his own
time--toward observer (2). Those signals have been labeled A, B,
C, D, and E and are directed radially away from the star's surface
by (1). A glance at Fig. 6.3 shows that signals A and B will arrive at (2) at about the same time difference with which they de-
parted (1). Signal C, on the other hand, will arrive considerably
delayed due to the increased influence of the gravitational field
(i.e., the inward tilting of the light cone). Just as he crosses
the Schwarzschild radius, (1) sends signal D, which, however,
never arrives at (2) since it will be trapped at $r = R$ (vertical
edge of the light cone). The final signal E has no chance at all
to escape from $r < R$. In fact after a relatively short time, this
signal will fall into the singularity $r = 0$. This discussion demonstrates that the collapse when observed from a distance will
appear to slow down gradually until it stops entirely when reaching the Schwarzschild radius: a signal sent at that moment will
reach the observer only after an infinite time (more precisely, a
signal that (1) sends from a radius $r = R(1 + \varepsilon)$, $\varepsilon \ll 1$, will
reach (2) at time $\tau \approx -(R/c)$ ℓn ε.

As far as (2) is concerned, the collapsing star never quite
reaches the Schwarzschild radius, i.e., it never becomes a real
"black hole" from which no information can be transmitted outwards. The luminosity of the star, however, decreases rapidly
since the light will be more and more red-shifted the closer to
the Schwarzschild radius it is emitted. A further reduction in
the luminosity results from the fact that the photons emitted at
equal time periods at (1) will reach (2) at ever increasing time
periods. Detailed calculations reveal that the luminosity L of
the star during the final phase of the collapse diminishes
according to

$$L = \text{const } e^{-t/\tau} \tag{6.11}$$

the characteristic time being $\tau = R/c$. For a star with mass $M \approx$
$10M_\odot$, we have $R \approx 30$ km and $\tau \approx 10^{-4}$ sec. According to our above

discussion the total collapse of a star is forever hidden from a distant observer; instead the star seems to remain eternally at its Schwarzschild radius. Its luminosity, however, drops to zero within fractions of a second, thereby justifying the term "black hole," which has been adopted in the Western literature. The Russians, on the other hand, use the term "frozen star," which reflects the apparent freezing of the star at the Schwarzschild radius.

Events that take place within the confines of the Schwarzschild radius will remain forever inaccessible to the outside observer (2) since no signal can possibly escape from within that radius. This fact leads to two concepts: (1) the surface of the "frozen star," which is a sphere with radius R, is called the star's *event horizon*. It can be thought of as a one-way membrane, allowing outside signals to cross inside, but preventing signals from inside the sphere to emerge outside. (2) If observer (2) could watch the entire collapse to the very end, we would be dealing with a *naked singularity*, i.e., an observable singularity. The existence of a nonzero event horizon shows, however, that black holes are *not* naked singularities. In fact, general relativity forbids the existence of naked singularities ("law of cosmic censorship").

Problem 6.3: Is the Singularity Avoidable?

Our discussion so far was based on the assumption that stars collapse in free fall. However, as the density increases, forces (like electron pressure, neutron pressure, etc.) arise that might well modify the course of the collapse. Show that once the star has collapsed to within its Schwarzschild radius, no finite force will be able to prevent the star from collapsing to a point thus forming a singularity. [Hint: note that forces can alter the world line of a material particle only within its light cone $(v < c)$!]

Problem 6.4: Density at the Schwarzschild Radius

Make a table containing the density that different masses reach at their Schwarzschild radii. What is this density for a galaxy? What conclusions can be drawn from this exercise?

THE GRAVITATIONAL FIELD OF BLACK HOLES

Following the exponential decay of the electromagnetic radiation of a collapsing star, the gravitational field remains as the only observable effect that hints at the existence of a black hole. Near the Schwarzschild radius the field cannot be described by Newton's theory. For our purposes, though, we only have to apply a slight modification to Newton's theory in order to derive the phenomena predicted by general relativity.

Let us recall the familiar derivation of the motion of a body with mass m in the gravitational field of a star. Using polar coordinates r, ϕ we can describe the motion by applying Kepler's law of areas

$$r^2 \dot{\phi} = l = \text{const} \tag{6.12}$$

and the energy law

$$\frac{\dot{r}^2}{2} + V_N(r) = \frac{E}{m} \tag{6.13}$$

Here the dots indicate time derivatives, l is the angular momentum (relative to unit mass) of the object, E its energy, and m its mass. The effective potential

$$V_N(r) = -\frac{GM}{r} + \frac{l^2}{2r^2} \tag{6.14}$$

consists of a gravitational potential and a centrifugal term.

According to general relativity, these equations must be modified as follows: the time derivatives (dots) must refer to the object's own time (i.e., time as measured by a clock that moves with the object). Furthermore, a different effective potential

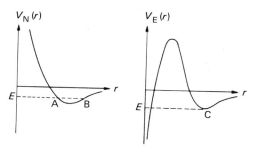

Fig. 6.4. Effective potential in Newton's and Einstein's gravitational theories.

$$V_E(r) = -\frac{GM}{r} + \frac{l^2}{2r^2} - \frac{Rl^2}{2r^3}$$

(6.15)

has to be used. Among other applications, Eqs. (6.12), (6.13), and (6.15) allow the exact calculation of the perihelion shift which we covered in Chapter 2.

Figure 6.4 compares the two effective potentials V_N and V_E used in Newton's and Einstein's gravitational theories, respectively. Here, we have assumed that $l \neq 0$, since for $l = 0$ we have $V_N = V_E$. In other words, in the case of a purely radial collapse toward the center (for which $l = 0$) we may use Newton's potential V_N, but we still must replace absolute time by the object time s of the collapsing object. The dashed line in the left part of Fig. 6.4 indicates the energy associated with an elliptic orbit that varies between radii A and B. The right-hand figure indicates the energy corresponding to a circular orbit. The only stable circular orbit occurs at one value of r (point C in the figure).[1]

----

[1] *Of course, circular orbits exist for V_N, just as elliptic orbits exist for V_E. We might mention that the maximum of $V_E(r)$ corresponds to an unstable circular orbit. The slightest perturbation will lead to an inward or outward spiraling motion.*

Given the angular momentum l (i.e., given the potential V_E) we know that the circular orbit has the lowest energy. How low can this energy be? This question is of practical interest since this is precisely the binding energy that can be emitted (as radiation) by an object circling the black hole. More realistically, we may imagine an object that circles the black hole at a great distance, emitting radiation, and slowly spiraling inwards as it loses energy.

Calculations (compare Problem 6.5) show that the highest possible binding energy of a particle of mass m, circling the black hole, amounts to $E = -0.055mc^2$ according to Einstein's theory. In other words, as the particle spirals inwards toward the center (black hole) it can only radiate 5.5% of its rest energy. After reaching a radius $r = 3R$ the circular orbit becomes unstable, and the particle falls inwards almost radially (see Fig. 6.5).

The result we have just obtained is directly opposed to the Newtonian predictions, which say that we can always reach a stable circular orbit with arbitrary small r by choosing a sufficiently small l. Thus, any multiple of the rest energy mc^2 can be radiated away while the particle spirals inwards!

In classical physics a particle freely falling in the gravitational field of a mass point could be viewed as a perpetuum mobile, since an inexhaustible source of energy would exist. The

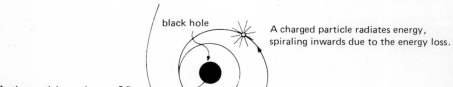

black hole

A charged particle radiates energy, spiraling inwards due to the energy loss.

As the particle reaches $r = 3R$ it falls radially toward the center (black hole) since there exist no stable circular orbits.

Fig. 6.5. Motion of a particle near a black hole.

following two problems will demonstrate how this situation is avoided by general relativity.

Problem 6.5: Circular Orbits around Black Holes

For a circular orbit we find $E = V_E(r)$ since $\dot{r} = 0$. Also, we have

$$dV_E/dr = 0$$

i.e., the potential is at a minimum. Show that this last condition leads to

$$l^2 = c^2 R r^2 (2r - 3R)^{-1}$$

which implies that the angular momentum l is only finite for $r > (3/2)R$. Substituting the above expression for l^2, we find

$$E(r) = mc\ \frac{R}{r}\frac{r - 2R}{2r - 3R}$$

Furthermore, for stable circular orbits we must have

$$d^2 V_E/dr^2 > 0$$

Show that this is only satisfied for $r > 3R$, and that $E(3R) = -mc^2/18$ is the maximal possible binding energy of a particle on a stable circular orbit.

Problem 6.6: Radial Fall

Classically, we can gain an arbitrary amount of energy by slowly lowering a particle (tied to a rope) into the gravitational field of a mass point, since a potential energy

$$E_R(r) = -m\frac{MG}{r} = -\frac{mc^2}{2}\frac{R}{r}$$

becomes available, and $\lim_{r \to 0} E(r) = \infty$. Why is this not possible in general relativity, and what limit exists for $E_R(r)$?

ROTATING BLACK HOLES

Our discussion of the theory of black holes has one important flaw, which we shall deal with in this section: we only considered the collapse of a spherically symmetric nonrotating star. This, however, is an ideal case, which is never realized in nature. How valid are the results that were obtained for the ideal case, when applied to the more realistic collapse?

Surprisingly, theoretical research in recent years has shown that the realistic collapse is not significantly different from the idealized model. The reason is--simply speaking--the strength of the gravitational field that causes the breakdown of most structures. For instance, we know that neutron stars have very intensive magnetic fields. Black holes, however, will not be surrounded by a magnetic field since such a field will fall toward the singularity due to the intense gravity, thereby vanishing within fractions of a second. Essentially the same arguments apply to any perturbations of the star from a sphere (or, for rotating stars from the geoidal shape). Such deviations are not able to withstand the gravitational pull, so that we will be dealing with perfectly spherical objects.

These examples should suffice in convincing the reader that a black hole must be a very simply structured object, completely describable by very few parameters. In fact, combined work of B. Carter, S. Hawking, W. Israel, and D. C. Robinson has recently led to the proof of the following theorem:

> The most general black hole is characterized by only three parameters: mass, angular momentum, electric charge. Any other physical properties of the collapsing star are lost during the collapse.

This theorem is also known as "a black hole has no hair" theorem.

Mass and electric charge of a black hole can be detected through the gravitational and electromagnetic field, respectively. In what way, however, does the angular momentum manifest itself to an outside observer? How does it act on particles and their orbits? This question is important since it is quite probable that the angular momentum plays a very important role during the collapse; we only have to remember how essential it was for pulsars.

The answer to the above questions is based on the (highly idealized) construction shown in Fig. 6.6. Let us assume a rotating black hole has been found somewhere in space. In order to study it, a giant steel frame is being constructed around the black hole. The frame is anchored "at infinity," in other words, far away from the black hole the frame forms an inertial system.

By measuring the lengths of the struts in this frame we can determine the spatial geometry in the neighborhood of the black hole, thereby verifying our results of Chapter 2. A number of clocks also enable us to obtain the influence of the mass on the speed of clocks. In addition, small test masses m suspended by springs are measuring the local gravitational field, while small test charges e can detect any electric charge that might be produced by the collapsing star.

Finally, we have attached a number of small gyros to the rigid frame. It is well known that gyros always tend to maintain a fixed direction in space. The gyrocompass, for instance, is based on precisely this property. Surprisingly, near the rotating black

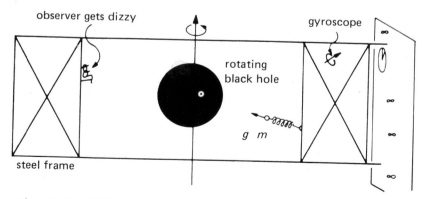

Fig. 6.6. Effects in the neighborhood of a rotating black hole.

hole the axis of each gyro will rotate against the rigidly anchored steel frame. According to calculations made by Thirring
and Lense (Thirring-Lense effect, 1919) the angular velocity ω of
the gyro axis will be

$$\omega = \frac{G}{r^3} \frac{3(Lx)x - Lr^2}{r^2} \tag{6.16}$$

where L is the angular momentum of the black hole. Thus, a rotating black hole will drag along its surrounding local inertial
system (as defined by the gyro axes), causing it to rotate with
respect to the steel frame, which represents the global structure
of space. This drag effect is one of the most surprising and interesting effects predicted by general relativity, and applies
equally to any other rotating objects like, e.g., the earth, but
on a much tinier scale.

The following fact is of significance for any experimental
attempts to discover black holes: a mass m orbiting a rotating
black hole can have a binding energy E up to 42% of its rest mass
(i.e., $E = 0.42mc^2$). In other words, if matter falls into a rotating black hole, up to 42% of its rest mass may be converted into
energy!

EXPLODING BLACK HOLES

The most significant characteristic of black holes is the fact
that light and matter can fall into a black hole but can never be
retrieved once they have crossed the Schwarzschild radius. Surprisingly, this basic fact is only valid within the framework of
classical physics. In 1974, Steven Hawking in a famous work demonstrated that black holes display considerably different properties when studied quantum mechanically. Hawking's main result
asserts that quantum-mechanical effects can lead to an emission of
light and matter. However, this "Hawking effect" is measurable
only in the case of black holes with a radius comparable to that
of an elementary particle ("mini-black hole").

The physical basis of this effect lies in the pair creation of
virtual particles that, according to the fundamental ideas of
quantum field theory, takes place continuously and everywhere in
space. The uncertainty relation $\Delta E\ \Delta t \approx \hbar$ makes it possible that
for very small times (Δt very small), the energy (ΔE) can be
raised sufficiently to create a pair of particles, one being the
anti-particle of the other. Under normal conditions both particles will immediately annihilate each other, justifying the term
"virtual particles." On the other hand, if this creation process
takes place close to a black hole then one particle could fall
through the Schwarzschild radius into the singularity in time to
escape annihilation. The second particle will then become a
"real" particle that will be radiated away from the black hole.
The energy necessary for the creation of this real particle is
supplied by the energy of the black hole. Withdrawing this energy
will reduce the total mass of the black hole.

This process may also be interpreted as the creation of a pair
of particles--one with negative, and one with positive energy. If
the particle with negative energy falls into the black hole, its
partner with positive energy will be radiated into space. As a
result, mass and energy of the black hole decrease.

Hawking's calculations showed that this type of radiation by
black holes has surprisingly simple properties. In fact, it has
all properties of "thermal radiation," familiar to students of
thermodynamics. Its temperature is linked to the mass of the
black hole in a simple relationship. We can use Wien's displacement law to estimate temperature and intensity of this radiation.
Wien's law says that thermal radiation of temperature T contains
mainly photons whose wavelength λ is given by

$$\lambda T \approx \hbar c/k \tag{6.17}$$

where k is Boltzmann's constant. The wavelength of the radiation
emitted by a black hole must depend in some straightforward fash-
ion on the geometry of the black hole. Since the only geometric

quantity of a black hole is its Schwarzschild radius R, we can expect the radiation to consist mostly of wavelengths for which $\lambda \approx R$. With this assumption we can compute the "temperature" of the black hole:

$$T \approx \frac{\hbar c}{k\lambda} \approx \frac{\hbar c^3}{kGM} \approx 10^{24} \ \text{K}/(M/\text{kg}) \tag{6.18}$$

Black holes emit thermal radiation whose temperature is inversely proportional to the mass of the black hole.

In order to compute the radiation intensity emitted by a black hole we multiply the radiant energy of temperature T (known from thermodynamics) by the area $A \approx 4\pi R^2$ of the black hole:

$$P \approx c\frac{(kT)^4}{(\hbar c)^3} A \approx c\frac{\hbar c}{R^4} R^2 = \frac{\hbar c^6}{G^2 M^2} \tag{6.19}$$

In other words, black holes with small mass will have a high temperature, thus emitting very intensive radiation. Numerically, mass and radiation intensity are connected by

$$P \approx 10^{38} \ \text{W}/(M/\text{kg})^2 \tag{6.20}$$

The emission of thermal radiation causes a constant, slow decrease in the mass of the black hole. Using the equation $Pt = Mc^2$, we can estimate the duration of the radiation:

$$t \approx \frac{Mc^2}{P} \approx \frac{G^2 M^3}{\hbar c^4} \approx 10^{-20} \ \text{sec}(M/\text{kg})^3 \tag{6.21}$$

These results indicate that the Hawking effect for black holes with several solar masses leads to negligible temperatures and radiation intensities. Small black holes, on the other hand, could display an astrophysically significant radiation intensity, lasting, however, for only a very short time. The question then arises how such small black holes could have been formed. After all, the gravitational collapse discussed earlier has always led to black holes whose mass is at least as large as the Chandrasekhar mass. We could imagine, however, that smaller black holes were formed during the earlier phases of the universe, approximately 10 billion years ago. The discussion in Chapter 10 will show that the density of the universe was very high at that time, so that collapsing regions of matter could have ended up as very tiny black holes. Of particular interest are black holes with masses of $M \approx 10^{12}$ kg whose lifetime according to Eq.(6.21) would be $t \approx 10^{10}$ years. We can envision the following scenario: black holes that were created in the initial phase of the universe live through billions of years by emitting radiation with an intensity of $P \approx 10^{14}$ W. During that time their mass gradually decreases while their temperature rises. If the initial mass of such a black hole happened to be $M \approx 10^{12}$ kg then we should expect its temperature and radiation intensity to increase rapidly today, ending its life in an explosion that would result in an intensive burst of photons in the x-ray regime and of other particles. So far, the search for such bursts of radiation has not been successful, leaving us with the conclusion that not too many of these mini-black holes were formed in the early universe.

CHAPTER 7

THE SEARCH FOR BLACK HOLES

During the decade 1963-1973 theoretical investigations into
gravitational collapse and black hole formation progressed quite
rapidly, yet it was not until 1969 that serious attempts were made
to empirically verify the existence of such exotic objects. In
particular, one had to look for methods that would enable one to
detect black holes with astronomical instruments. Clearly, this
is not an easy task in view of the fact that black holes are
characterized by not emitting any light! There is one theoretical
prediction, however, that comes to our aid. Gaseous matter that
is drawn into the black hole by the immense gravitational pull
will be heated before falling through the Schwarzschild radius.
The resulting radiation led (in 1972/1973) to the discovery of an
object in CYGNUS X1 that most astronomers believe to be a black
hole.

METHODS FOR DETECTING BLACK HOLES

In order to discover black holes, three methods have been proposed in the last few years (Fig. 7.1):

(a) A binary system consisting of a normal star and a black
hole, circling each other at a large distance (large, when compared against the star's diameter) may be detected through the
Doppler shift of the star's spectral lines. We discuss this method in the following section, by studying the system ε-Aurigae.

(b) A binary system in which the distance between the star
and the black hole is comparable to the star's diameter gives rise

112

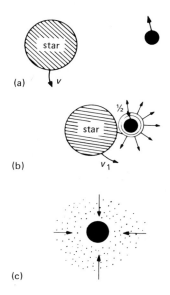

Fig. 7.1. Methods for the detection of black holes. (a) Star and black hole: optical search. (b) Star and very close black hole: gas capture and resulting emission of x rays. (c) Single black hole surrounded by interstellar dust: gas capture and emission of light.

to a new phenomenon: gas from the star will be drawn into the black hole. This, in turn, will lead to a temperature increase of several million degrees, causing the gas to emit x rays, which should be detectable with the methods of x-ray astronomy. Results that were obtained in 1972/1973 will be discussed in later sections.

(c) Even single black holes give away their existence by gradually capturing interstellar gas. The gas again becomes heated and emits light. This light is emitted *before* the gas reaches the Schwarzschild radius, so there is no contradiction to our earlier characterization of black holes! Due to the low density of interstellar gas (in regions of ionized hydrogen, $\rho \approx 10^{-21}$ kg/m^3), the phenomena are not nearly as spectacular as those occuring in the binary systems described under (b). In fact, the interstellar gas that flows steadily into the black hole merely reaches a few thousand degrees before crossing the event horizon at the Schwarzschild radius. For a black hole of ten solar masses, the emitted radiation will have approximately the same intensity and spectral distribution as a certain class of white dwarfs (DC-dwarfs). We therefore must leave room for the possibility that some objects that have been classified as white dwarfs are in reality black holes that "feed" on interstellar matter. Since the radiation properties of both objects are highly similar, no decision can be made at this time, and hence this method must at least for now be abandoned.

EPSILON AURIGAE

The method depicted in Fig. 7.1a appears to be the most straightforward procedure for detecting black holes. If we can locate a binary system in which one component is visible and the other has a mass exceeding the upper mass limit for neutron stars, then we must be dealing with a black hole. After all, we learned in Chapter 4 that white dwarfs and neutron stars must have masses below the Chandrasekhar limit.

These arguments sound quite convincing. Unfortunately, the best-known binary system ε-Aurigae has taught us that this method must be approached with caution.

ε-Aurigae is a star of magnitude $m = 3.1$ and can be seen with the naked eye. It is shown on every map of stars. A periodic Doppler shift of its spectral lines indicates that the star is one component of a binary system with invisible second component. The magnitude of the Doppler shift allows us to determine its orbital velocity:

$$v_1 = 14 \text{ km/sec} \tag{7.1}$$

The orbital period τ is

$$\tau = 9883 \text{ days} = 27.1 \text{ years} \tag{7.2}$$

Given those two data, we can compute the so-called mass function of the binary system (see Fig. 7.2). Both components (one visible, the other possibly a black hole) move around their common center of gravity CG on orbits whose major semiaxes a_1 and a_2 satisfy

$$a_2 : a_1 = M_1 : M_2 = v_2 : v_1 \tag{7.3}$$

The observed velocity v_1 is expressible in terms of a_1 and the period τ:

$$v_1 = \frac{2\pi a_1}{\tau} \sin i \tag{7.4}$$

Here the quantity i is the (unknown) angle between the orbital plane and the observational direction (to earth; see Fig. 7.3). To be precise, Eq. (7.4) is really valid for circular orbits. However, as it turns out the systems discussed here all seem to have nearly circular orbits.

We may extract further information about the system by using Kepler's law:

$$\tau = 2\pi a^{3/2} (GM_1 + GM_2)^{-1/2}$$

$$a = a_1 + a_2 \tag{7.5}$$

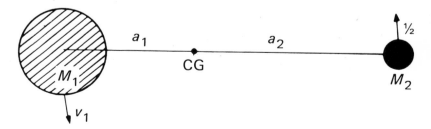

Fig. 7.2. Calculation of the mass function of a binary system (CG = center of gravity).

Fig. 7.3. *Geometry of the orbital plane associated with a binary system.*

Equations (7.3)-(7.5) yield

$$a_1 = a \frac{M_2}{M_1 + M_2} \tag{7.6}$$

$$v_1 = \frac{2\pi a}{\tau} \frac{M_2}{M_1 + M_2} \sin i \tag{7.7}$$

Elimination of a from (7.5) and (7.7) leads to the *mass function* M of the system:

$$M = \frac{M_2^3}{(M_1 + M_2)^2} \sin^3 i = \frac{v_1^3 \tau}{2\pi G} \tag{7.8}$$

Since the mass function is determined by v_1 and τ, we may calculate it from observations of just one component of a binary system. For ε-Aurigae we find $M = 3.12 M_\odot$. If we can deduce the mass M_1 of the visible component from spectroscopic measurements, if we can further somehow obtain information about sin i, then Eq. (7.8) allows us to compute the mass M_2 of the invisible partner.

For ε-Aurigae, astronomers have estimated a mass $M_1 \approx 12\text{-}25 M_\odot$ based on the spectral type of the star. There are also very narrow limits for sin i since ε-Aurigae is an eclipsing binary system. Every 27 years the star is partially obscured by its (invisible) partner. During the eclipse the luminosity of the star drops by a factor of 2, remaining at that low level for 360 days (see Fig. 7.4).

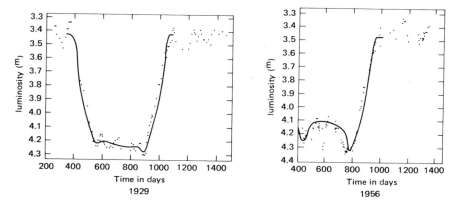

Fig. 7.4. Luminosity data for ε-Aurigae during the eclipses of 1929 and 1956 (the curves are the result of Wilson's model).

The very existence of these eclipses implies that $\sin i \approx 1$ since only then can the two stars obscure each other. If we substitute this value as well as our estimate for M_1 into Eq. (7.8), we obtain

$$M_2 \approx 12\text{-}18 M_\odot \tag{7.9}$$

as the mass of the invisible partner. Since M_2 exceeds the Chandrasekhar limit by far, one is tempted to conclude that the invisible object must be a black hole.

We know, however, that black holes are very small objects. A black hole of mass $M_2 = 15 M_\odot$ has a radius of only 15 km, and therefore cannot possibly obscure a significant area of ε-Aurigae.

In order to resolve this paradox, we have to assume that the black hole is surrounded by a ring or halo of semitransparent material, as shown in Fig. 7.5. This apparently arbitrary assumption (based on the work of Wilson and Cameron) does solve the problem of the unusual luminosity curves of ε-Aurigae. If we assume that a second (dark) star causes the eclipse (rather than a black hole surrounded by a halo), we end up with luminosity curves that look totally different from those shown in Fig. 7.4, which

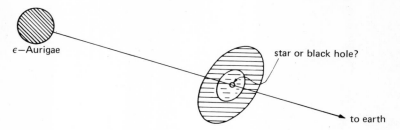

Fig. 7.5. Model of ε-Aurigae according to Wilson and Cameron.

are very unusual for eclipsing binaries (see Fig. 7.6). The model
of a black hole with a semitransparent ring, on the other hand,
leads to a very good explanation of the eclipses of ε-Aurigae.
The reader only has to compare the theoretical luminosity curves
that have been drawn in Fig. 7.4.

A black hole, surrounded by a halo, is therefore a possible
model for ε-Aurigae. Is this model unique, however? Are there no
other explanations of the eclipses? Unfortunately, the above
arguments do contain a serious gap. If the luminosities of the
two components of a (spectroscopic) binary system differ by a
factor of 10 or more, then only one component will be visible,
outshining the other one. Could it be that the invisible partner
of ε-Aurigae is a normal star with a ten times weaker luminosity
than the main star? This is indeed possible if both stars have
the maximal estimated mass, i.e., $M_1 = 25M_\odot$ and $M_2 = 18M_\odot$. In
this case, M_2 is sufficiently smaller than M_1, resulting in a
luminosity difference by a factor of 10.

How can we decide between the two possible partners for ε-
Aurigae: black hole or normal star? The answer could be hidden
in Fig. 7.4. The eclipse of 1929 shows a light curve with a very
flat minimum; in 1956, the luminosity increases after an initial
minimum (this could be explained by a slight change in the trans-
parency of the halo), and then shows a sharp and brief drop near
the center of the curve. This drop in the luminosity cannot be
predicted by the model of Wilson and Cameron (Fig. 7.5), and might

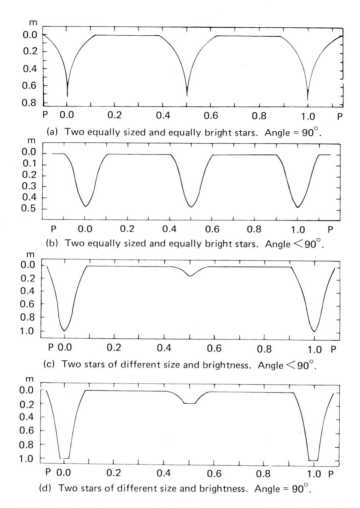

(a) Two equally sized and equally bright stars. Angle = 90°.

(b) Two equally sized and equally bright stars. Angle < 90°.

(c) Two stars of different size and brightness. Angle < 90°.

(d) Two stars of different size and brightness. Angle = 90°.

*Fig. 7.6. The typical luminosity curves of eclipsing binaries
deviate significantly from the curves in Fig. 7.4.*

point to a star that is located at the center of the halo instead
of a black hole.

We shall have to wait for the next eclipse in 1983, which
might allow us to decide whether or not the invisible partner of
ε-Aurigae is indeed a black hole.

BINARY SYSTEMS AS X-RAY SOURCES

If the distance between the partners of a binary system becomes comparable to the stellar radius of one component, a new phenomenon enters the picture: gas will start to flow from the surface of one component to its companion. This mass exchange can be observed in numerous binary systems and can reach up to $10^{-6} M_\odot$ per year.

In case one component of such a close binary system is a neutron star or a black hole, the gas exchange will unleash tremendous energies within a small region. The gas is heated to several million degrees, and emits x rays. This situation is depicted in Fig. 7.7. Theoretical studies of the dynamics of close binaries have shown that there exists a critical surface around the centers of mass of the two components. This critical surface forms a "figure 8." The two lobes surrounding the two stars are known as the Roche lobes, while the point at which they cross is the inner Lagrange point (L_1 in Fig. 7.7). If a star fills its Roche lobe, gas will start to flow from its surface through the inner Lagrange point L_1 to its companion. Coriolis forces will

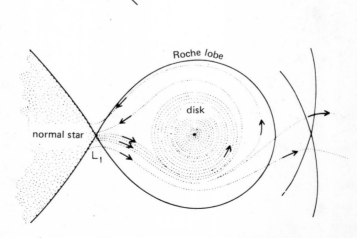

Fig. 7.7. Gas flow in a binary system.

force the gas into a circular orbit around the second component, and a rotating gaseous disk (the "accretion disk") will form around the second star (or the black hole). The velocity profile in these accretion disks bears a close resemblance to that of rotating galaxies; in particular, the velocity is given by

$$v^2 = GM_2/r$$

Since $v \propto r^{-1/2}$, the disk does not rotate rigidly (rigid rotation would occur if $v \propto r$), instead, the inner regions rotate much faster than the outer regions. The resulting friction causes heating of the gas, which then emits light and x rays.

Due to the loss of energy, the gas will gradually spiral inwards. The inner edge R_1 of the gas disk either coincides with the surface of the secondary star (unless instabilities arise earlier) or, in case of a black hole, with the radius of the smallest stable circular orbit.

The luminosity of the gas disk depends on the amount of inflowing matter per second, and also on the fraction ε of this mass that can--according to $E = mc^2$--be converted into energy. In order to estimate ε, we shall use the results obtained in our discussion of the gravitational field around black holes (Chapter 6). For a particle m, which orbits the mass M_2 on a circular orbit of radius R_1, the binding energy is given by

$$E \approx \varepsilon \times mc^2 \approx (R/R_1)mc^2$$

where R is the Schwarzschild radius of the mass M_2. This energy can be emitted as electromagnetic radiation, while the particle slowly spirals toward the radius R_1. Again, it is the ratio of Schwarzschild radius to radius that determines ε.

Consequently, for a gas disk around a normal star, approximately 10^{-6} of its mass can be converted into radiation; for a white dwarf, about 10^{-4}; for a neutron star, about 10^{-1}; and if the partner is a black hole, about 5 to 40%.

TABLE 7.1

Object	ε	L (W)
Normal star	10^{-6}	10^{25}
White dwarf	10^{-4}	10^{27}
Neutron star	10^{-1}	10^{30}
Black hole	0.05-0.40	10^{30}

Assuming a mass transfer of about $10^{-9} M_\odot$ per year (this assumption can be substantiated further), we have entered the luminosity L of the gas disk in Table 7.1 ($10^{-9} M_\odot$ per year corresponds to a radiation output of 10^{31} W with total conversion into energy, $\varepsilon = 1$).

The radiation spectrum can be crudely estimated if we assume that black body radiation (thermal spectrum) is emitted. In this case, the luminosity of the gas disk is given by

$$L \approx \sigma R^2 T^4 \qquad (7.10)$$

where $\sigma = 5.67 \times 10^{-8}$ W/m^2 is the Stefan-Boltzmann constant, and R is a characteristic radius of the disk, which we set at 5 to 10 times the stellar radius. Dividing Eq.(7.10) by $L_\odot \approx \sigma R_\odot^2 T_\odot^4$ (this relation connects luminosity and temperature for the sun), we find

$$\frac{L}{L_\odot} = \left(\frac{R}{R_\odot}\right)^2 \left(\frac{T}{T_\odot}\right)^4 \qquad (7.11)$$

Since L can be obtained from Table 7.1, while the radii can be estimated to within an order of magnitude, Eq.(7.11) can be used to compute the temperature of the gas disk. The mean energy E_γ of the photons in thermal radiation is proportional to the temperature (Wien's displacement law), and has a value of $E_{\gamma\odot} \approx 1$ eV for the sun (frequencies being $\nu_\odot \approx 10^{15}$ Hz from $E_{\gamma\odot} = h\nu_\odot$). Hence

TABLE 7.2

Object	L (W)	R (m)	E
Normal star	10^{25}	10^9	1 eV
White dwarf	10^{27}	10^7	10 eV
Neutron star	10^{30}	10^5	1 keV
Black hole	10^{30}	10^5	1 keV

$$\frac{E_\gamma}{1 \text{ eV}} \approx \frac{\nu}{\nu_\odot} \approx \frac{T}{T_\odot} \approx \left(\frac{L}{L_\odot}\right)^{1/4} \left(\frac{R_\odot}{R}\right)^{1/2} \tag{7.12}$$

Using the luminosity L from Table 7.1, and the above-mentioned approximation for R, we can summarize our results in Table 7.2.

The gaseous disks around neutron stars and black holes are characterized by emitting x rays in the keV regime.

Such energetic x rays cannot develop if the gas is captured by a normal star or a white dwarf since those objects are large and have relatively weak gravitational fields. Consequently,

Binary systems that emit highly energetic x rays must contain either a neutron star or a black hole.

Although these results have brought us one important step closer to our search for black holes, how can we differentiate between neutron stars and black holes? This question is analyzed in the following comparison:

Gas Capture and X-Ray Emission by

Neutron star	Black hole
Mass $M < 3M_\odot$ always	Mass $M > 3M_\odot$ possible and expected
Strong magnetic field	No magnetic field
Regular x-ray pulses due to lighthouse effect as discussed for pulsars	Irregular fluctuations fo the x-ray emission

The mass of the x-ray source as well as the regularity of the emitted radiation provide us with two criteria that should enable us to differentiate between the two possibilities.

Experimental results from x-ray astronomy have shown that both kinds of x-ray sources--regular pulses and irregular ones--exist. In the next two sections we shall discuss one source of each type.

HERCULES Xl -- A NEUTRON STAR

Until a few years ago, the earth's atmosphere presented an insurmountable obstacle for x-ray astronomy. Figure 7.8 shows that particularly the x-ray radiation in the keV regime will be absorbed in the upper atmosphere. This fact is quite essential for the existence of x-ray astronomers (life on earth could not exist without the atmospheric absorption of such radiation), but highly detrimental for their professional activity. Only after the advent of space rockets and satellites did x-ray astronomy in the

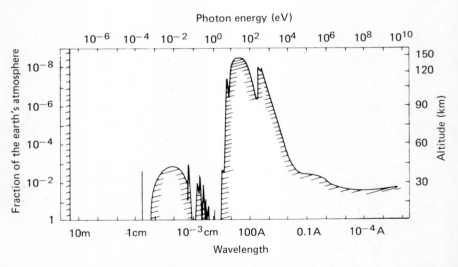

Fig. 7.8. Altitude in the earth's atmosphere (i.e., fraction of the atmosphere) at which arriving radiation of the given wavelength has been reduced to 10% of its initial intensity (through atmospheric absorption).

keV regime become feasible; and only satellites permitted longer-term observations and precise bearings on the location of the x-ray source.

Of particular importance is the satellite *Uhuru*, which was launched on December 12, 1970 and has so far discovered more than 100 x-ray sources of which two will be discussed in detail here.

In this section we shall describe the x-ray source known as Hercules X1. Figure 7.9 shows its x-ray signal. This signal has all the typical characteristics of a pulsar. The pulses occur at the regular period of

$$\tau_1 = 1.23782 \text{ sec}$$

$$(7.13)$$

which we can identify with the rotational period of the neutron star (just as we discussed in the chapter on pulsars).

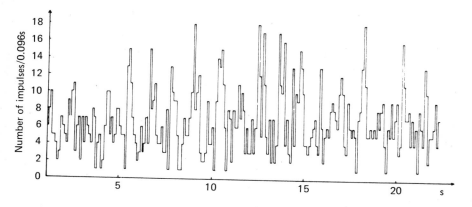

Fig. 7.9. The x-ray signal from Hercules X1.

The x-ray signals exhibit a secondary periodicity: after every

$$\tau = 1.700167 \text{ days} \tag{7.14}$$

the pulses cease for a couple of hours. Apparently, this x-ray source is one component of a binary system whose normal component periodically obscures the x-ray component. The high precision with which τ_1 could be measured led to the subsequent discovery of Doppler shifts in the periodicity of the signals, which were caused by the source's orbital motion at a velocity of

$$v_2 \sin i = 169 \text{ km/sec} \tag{7.15}$$

Equations (7.14) and (7.15) enable us to compute the mass function of the binary system:

$$M = \frac{M_1^{\,3}}{(M_1 + M_2)^2} \sin^3 i = 0.85 M_\odot \tag{7.16}$$

Here M_2 is the mass of the x-ray source. Knowledge of M gives us the (projected) orbital radius

$$a \sin i = 4 \times 10^9 \text{ m} \tag{7.17}$$

which is comparable to stellar radii (e.g., $R_\odot = 7 \times 10^8$ m). We are thus dealing with a close binary as discussed in the previous section.

After astronomers had agreed on those numerical results, a feverish search began for the (optical) star, which is being circled by the x-ray source. Finally in September 1972 John and Neta Bahcall could pinpoint a star "HZ Herculis," which displayed fluctuations in luminosity and color at a period that precisely coincided with (7.14). (See Fig. 7.10.)

The companion to the x-ray source had indeed been found, and in due time the cause of the variations in luminosity and color became clear, too: the intense x-ray radiation heats up one side of HZ Herculis. This side has a higher luminosity and appears

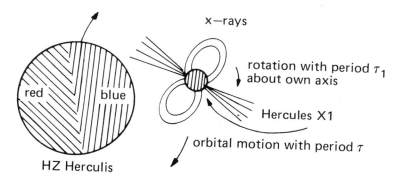

x—rays

rotation with period τ_1
about own axis

Hercules X1

orbital motion with period τ

red   blue

HZ Herculis

Fig. 7.10. Model of the system HZ Herculis and Hercules X1.

bluish, while the other side is of lower luminosity and shines
red. Spectroscopic measurements fixed the mass of HZ-Herculis at
M_1 = 1.6-2.5$M_\odot$, and detailed studies (which determined the angle
i of the orbital plane) led to a mass

$$M_2 \approx 0.9 M_\odot$$

of Hercules X1 (estimates of different authors vary from 0.5 to
1.3$M_\odot$). This is the first mass determination of a neutron star!
    The distance of HZ Herculis from earth can be deduced from the
spectral type of the star: it is about 20,000 light years. This
in turn allows us to estimate the luminosity of the x-ray source
to

$$L \approx 10^{30} \text{ W}$$

(7.18)

in agreement with our earlier estimates.

CYGNUS X1--A BLACK HOLE

    The x-ray source Cygnus X1 is located in the constellation
Swan. Its signal is fundamentally different from the highly regular pulses of the source in Hercules (Fig. 7.11). There is no
discernible periodicity and the signal fluctuates rapidly within
milliseconds, suggesting a very compact source of diameter less
than 10^4 km.

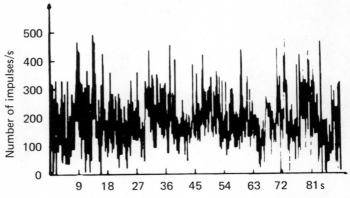

Fig. 7.11.   The x-ray signal from Cygnus X1.

Cygnus X1 shows no sign of being an eclipsing binary system. This fact together with the nonperiodicity of the x-ray signal does not even tell us whether this source is part of a binary system.

Only after a series of precision experiments pinpointed the exact location of the x-ray source, did astronomers find a star of thirteenth magnitude (known as HDE 22 6868, which is the number out of a star catalog) at that location (Fig. 7.12). In fact, this star even exhibited a Doppler shift! Observations of HDE 22 6868 led to

$$v_1 = 75 \text{ km/sec}, \qquad \tau = 5.6 \text{ days} \tag{7.19}$$

and thus to a mass function

$$M = \frac{M_2^3}{(M_1 + M_2)^2} \sin^3 i = 0.242 M_\odot \tag{7.20}$$

Studies of the spectrum of HDE 22 6868 suggested a super giant of mass $M_1 \approx 20\text{-}25 M_\odot$. Substituting this estimate into (7.20) yields M_2 (the mass of the x-ray source) as a function of sin i. The minimum occurs for sin $i = 1$, and has a value of $5.5 M_\odot$. Thus

$$M_2 > 5.5 M_\odot \tag{7.21}$$

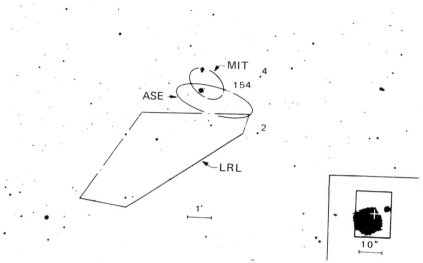

*Fig. 7.12. Determination of the position of the x-ray source
CYGNUS X1. This negative plate was photographed at Mount Wilson.
Satellite measurements of research teams from MIT, ASE (American
Science and Engineering), and LRL (Lawrence Radiation Laboratory)
resulted in the indicated three areas inside which each team suspected the x-ray source. As it turned out, HDE 22 6868 (which is
being orbited by CYGNUS X1) is the bright star in the intersection
of the regions predicted by MIT and ASE (compare the magnified
picture in the lower right corner).*

This mass significantly exceeds the upper mass limit for neutron
stars! Also, $\sin i = 1$ is incompatible with the fact that Cygnus
X1 shows no signs of periodic eclipses, and hence M_2 must be much
larger than the minimum given in (7.21). Detailed studies of the
system place the mass at

$$M_2 \approx 14 M_\odot$$

They also suggest $i \approx 27°$, a distance of 6000 light years from
earth, and an intensity of the x-ray emission of 10^{30} W. Thus

It is highly probable that Cygnus X1 is a black hole.

All the data agree with our expectations: irregular x-ray signal, a mass above $3M_\odot$, and finally the intensity of the x-ray emission.

There remain, however, some open questions: how can a star collapse totally to become a black hole without disrupting the binary system? In fact, Doppler measurements suggest an almost circular orbit of the system, even though we would expect a least a highly eccentric orbit as a result of the disruption of the binary after one partner has undergone complete gravitational collapse.

In any case, in view of these discoveries relativistic astrophysics promises to become one of the most intriguing fields of research in years to come!

BLACK HOLES IN GLOBULAR CLUSTERS AND GALAXIES

So far we have studied black holes whose masses were comparable to typical stellar masses. Observations conducted in the past few years have led to the belief that black holes of considerably higher masses might be lurking in the central regions of globular clusters and galaxies.

The first clues were found several years ago after conducting star counts in the globular clusters nearest to our Milky Way. A count of stars as a function of distance from the center of the cluster showed an unexpectedly high concentration of stars close to the center in three different clusters. This concentration could be explained through the presence of a black hole with several thousand solar masses.

Even more fascinating is the 1978 discovery concerning the galaxy M87 and the possible existence of a black hole of about 5 × $10^9 M_\odot$ in its center. The elliptic galaxy M87 had been the target of much interest for a long time since this active radio source lies relatively close to us and emits a beam of matter, radiating polarized light.

A photometric study of M87 showed a steep increase in the density of stars in a 4 light year neighborhood around the galactic center. But even at 100-fold distances the distribution of stars does not agree with the normal distributions found in other galaxies. Again, the intensive gravitational field of a monstrous black hole could explain the observational data.

This interpretation has been supported by another experiment. Measuring the widening of spectral lines of stars close to the center of M87 can lead to a determination of their velocity distribution. From

$$v^2/2 \approx MG/R \qquad\qquad (7.22)$$

we can compute the mass distribution within a given radius R around the galactic center. Comparing the mass with the photometrically measured luminosity showed that the mass contained in the central core of M87 is about ten times larger than would be expected from the total luminosity of the stars in that region. This is a further strong hint that a large dark object exists in the center of M87. From these data and the observed luminosity distribution we can calculate the mass of the hypothetical dark central object to about $5 \times 10^9 M_\odot$.

In summary, spectroscopic and photometric data suggest the existence of an immense black hole of about 5 billion solar masses in the center of M87. Confirmation of this hypothesis could lead to another fundamental revision of our astronomical and cosmological world model. Current theory cannot explain the formation of such an immense black hole in the center of a galaxy. Yet, the existence of such a black hole could--in addition to the data mentioned above--explain the intensive x-ray radiation that is emitted by M87 (5×10^{35} W). A mechanism similar to that discussed for CYGNUS X1 may be at work.

CHAPTER 8

GRAVITATIONAL WAVES

Gravitational waves are tiny oscillations (ripples) of space-time that propagate at the speed of light. Their existence was theoretically predicted by Albert Einstein in 1920 on the basis of his general theory of relativity. He thought, however, that their experimental detection would be impossible since any conceivable laboratory experiments would only lead to effects so subtle as to be nonmeasurable. As a result, the years 1920-1960 saw numerous theoretical speculations about gravitational waves being published, yet there were no serious attempts at measuring them.

In 1960 Professor Joseph Weber (University of Maryland) initiated experiments that at first seemed to have no chance of success. His intention was to detect and measure gravitational waves that might originate near the center of our galaxy. In order to properly evaluate these experiments we must first elaborate on the theoretical foundations of gravitational waves.

THE EMISSION OF GRAVITATIONAL WAVES

Before we can observe gravitational waves (or radiation), we have to study the conditions under which they arise and might be received. The situation is analogous to that of electromagnetic waves, and we shall therefore proceed with electrodynamics as our guide. There, the basic fact is

Accelerated charges emit electromagnetic waves, radiating an energy of

132

$$P = \frac{2}{3c^3} \sum_{\alpha=1}^{3} \ddot{p}_\alpha^{\,2} \qquad (8.1)$$

per unit time (total radiated power).

In this formula,

$$p_\alpha = \int d^3x \rho(x, t) x_\alpha \qquad (\alpha = 1,2,3) \qquad (8.2)$$

is the electric dipole moment of the charge distribution; $\rho(x, t)$ is the charge density. The dots in Eq.(8.1) refer to differentiation with respect to time t, as usual.

Examples based on formula (8.1) are radio transmitters, the "Bremsstrahlung" (x rays that are generated by the rapid deceleration of high-energy electrons), and synchroton radiation (emitted by particles that spiral with relativistic speed in magnetic fields). Formula (8.1) and its generalizations form the basis for the entire theory of electromagnetic radiation and are applied in quantum theory to compute the discrete and continuous spectra of atoms, while the classical applications include complicated arrangements of charges and antennas.

Analogously, but based on the field equations of general relativity, we obtain

Accelerated masses emit gravitational waves, radiating an energy of

$$P = \frac{G}{5c^5} \sum_{\alpha,\beta=1}^{3} \dddot{Q}_{\alpha\beta}^{\,2} \qquad (8.3)$$

per unit time (P = total radiated power).

Here,

$$Q_{\alpha\beta}(t) = \int \rho(x, t)(x_\alpha x_\beta - \frac{1}{3} \delta_{\alpha\beta} r^2) \, d^3x \qquad (8.4)$$

is the quadrupole moment of the mass distribution, $\rho(x, t)$ the mass density, and $\delta_{\alpha\beta}$ the Kronecker symbol ($\delta_{\alpha\beta}$ = 1 for $\alpha = \beta$; $\delta_{\alpha\beta}$ = 0 for $\alpha \neq \beta$).

The quadrupole moment of a mass distribution measures the deviation of the mass from a spherical shape, i.e., for spherical masses $Q_{\alpha\beta}$ = 0, so that spherical masses do not emit gravitational radiation.

Next we shall estimate the order of magnitude of gravitational waves that are emitted by systems in periodic motion (e.g., earth-sun system). In accordance with the rest of the book, we shall ignore precise numeric factors. Due to the periodicity of the motion, we are always dealing with a term sin ωt, resulting in a factor ω for each time derivative, so that we can rewrite formula (8.3) as

$$P \approx \frac{G}{c^5} \omega^6 \sum_{\alpha,\beta=1}^{3} Q_{\alpha\beta}^2 \tag{8.5}$$

According to Eq. (8.4), $Q_{\alpha\beta}$ for the system consisting of earth and sun is approximately

$$Q_{\alpha\beta} \approx mr^2 \tag{8.6}$$

where m is the earth's mass, and r the mean distance earth-sun. Since the sun is located at the origin of the coordinate system its mass does not contribute to the quadrupole moment.

Substituting (8.6) into Eq. (8.5) yields

$$P \approx \frac{G}{c^5} \omega^6 m^2 r^4 \tag{8.7}$$

This same formula can also be applied to estimate gravitational radiation emitted by other periodically moving systems (e.g., rotating rods). The smallness of the factor G/c^5 that is contained in Eq. (8.7) already hints at the fact that lab experiments will generate no noticeable emission of gravitational waves (compare Problem 8.1).

In order to get a feeling for the total radiated power of different astronomic objects we shall rewrite Eq.(8.7). First, we set $\omega = 2\pi/T$, T being the time for one orbit of the system. Then,

$$P \approx \frac{G}{c^5} \left(\frac{2\pi}{T}\right)^6 m^2 r^4 = \frac{G}{c^5} \left(\frac{2\pi r}{T}\right)^6 \frac{m^2}{r^2} \tag{8.8}$$

Now, $2\pi r$ is the circumference of the orbit (e.g., the earth's orbit), and $v = 2\pi r/T$ is the (mean) orbital velocity. From an earlier chapter we know that for a circular orbit in a gravitational field we have the stability condition

$$v^2 = MG/r \tag{8.9}$$

where M is the mass of the object at the center (e.g., the sun). Inserting this relation into Eq.(8.8) gives us

$$P \approx \frac{G}{c^5} v^6 \frac{m^2}{r^2} = \frac{G}{c^5} \left(\frac{MG}{r}\right)^3 \frac{m^2}{r^2}$$

or

$$P \approx \frac{c^5}{G} \left(\frac{MG}{rc^2}\right)^3 \left(\frac{mG}{rc^2}\right)^2 \tag{8.10}$$

Using the Schwarzschild radii $R_1 = 2MG/c^2$ and $R_2 = 2mG/c^2$ of the two masses, we can finally write the total radiated power of the system as

$$P \approx \frac{c^5}{G} \left(\frac{R_1}{r}\right)^3 \left(\frac{R_2}{r}\right)^2 \tag{8.11}$$

Since both the terms in parentheses are dimensionless, the expression c^5/G must have the dimension of power, i.e.,

$$c^5/G \approx 10^{52} \text{ W} \tag{8.12}$$

Compared to the light power of the sun (10^{26} W), this is a tremendous radiation power, which, of course, can only be realized in systems for which $R_1 \approx R_2 \approx r$. Examples of such systems might be two neutron stars, orbiting each other, or a neutron star during its collapse that is not perfectly spherical due to initial asymmetry. In any case, we see that *during the birth of neutron stars or black holes highly intensive gravitational waves can be emitted.* However, this enormous output of energy (8.12) can only be sustained for fractions of a second.

The gravitational wave length to be expected may be derived from the characteristic quantities of the system: both Schwarzschild radii and neutron star radii are of the order of several kilometers; hence we can expect wavelengths

$$\lambda = 10 \text{ km} \times c/v \approx 100 \text{ km} \tag{8.13}$$

since the final phase of the collapse proceeds at a speed of $v \approx c/10$. The corresponding frequency follows from $\lambda v = c$:

$$v \approx 3000 \text{ Hz} \tag{8.14}$$

On the basis of these results, the search for gravitational waves has been conducted in the kilohertz region.

Problem 8.1: Generation of Gravitational Waves

Using Eq.(8.7) calculate the gravitational radiation that is generated by typical experimental contraptions found in a laboratory (e.g., rotating rods). How much time passes until a noticeable fraction of their energy is lost through gravitational radiation?

Problem 8.2: Gravitational Waves in the Solar System

Compute the energy radiated away as gravitational waves by the earth on its orbit around the sun. Do the same for the moon's orbit around the earth. How much time passes until these bodies have radiated away 1% of the kinetic energy of their orbital motion?

DETECTION OF GRAVITATIONAL WAVES

As we saw, measurable gravitational waves are only generated by systems that are near their Schwarzschild radius (i.e., neutron stars and black holes). It is therefore not possible to build a sender-receiver type system in a laboratory. Rather, the search for gravitational waves must consist in designing a laboratory receiver that registers gravitational radiation emitted by astronomical objects. The expected frequency of the signals is given by Eq.(8.14), assuming that the waves are produced by collapsing stars of solar mass. The duration of the signals is estimated at fractions of a second.

In 1960 Joseph Weber began with the construction of a receiver for gravitational waves. His receiver was aimed at detecting a frequency of 1660 Hz. In principle this task is quite simple.

Just as any arrangement of electric charges capable of oscillating can serve as a receiver for electromagnetic waves, so can any arrangement of masses capable of oscillating be used as a receiver for gravitational waves. In both situations it is important to exploit *resonance phenomena* in order to arrive at sufficiently sensitive detectors.

Weber's experiment--duplicated in the last few years with slight modifications by a dozen different research teams--consists of a cylindrical detector (Fig. 8.1) with a length of 153 cm and a diameter of 50 cm. The cylinder is made of aluminum and weighs

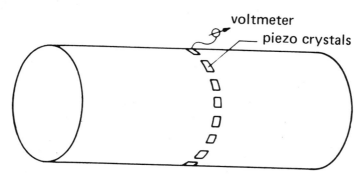

Fig. 8.1. Weber's detector for gravitational waves.

about one ton. A gravitational wave arriving vertically to the
cylinder axis will cause the mass to oscillate. The resonance
frequency of the detector is 1660 Hz, the bandwidth is minimal,
only 0.03 Hz, so that the detector will only respond to a very
narrow frequency band. Gravitational waves with a power of 10
W/m^2 arriving within this frequency band will cause the receiver
to respond. The amplitude of the cylinder's oscillation will then
be 10^{-16} m!

Weber's great achievement was his experimental verification of
such minute oscillations. This he did by attaching piezoelectric
quartzes around the circumference of the cylinder (Fig. 8.1). The
tiniest oscillations of the cylinder will give rise to electric
voltages in the quartzes that can be measured. The lower threshold of sensitivity is given by thermal noise. In view of this
fact, the sensitivity of future detectors will be increased by
having them operate at very low temperatures. Details can be
found in the next section.

Weber installed several of his detectors at Washington, D.C.,
and Chicago at a distance of about 1000 km. Most of the time the
recording graphs will only register thermal noise, but occasion-
ally the detectors at both locations will record simultaneous
jumps (so-called "coincidences"). During the years 1973 and 1974
Weber observed several coincidences daily at irregular intervals,
each signal lasting less than a second.

These observations stirred up much excitement, particularly
after Weber presented arguments that the signals recorded by him
may have emanated from the center of our galaxy. In order to be
detected, a signal must have an energy flux of about 10 J/m^2 within the bandwidth of the receiver. Since it is highly improbable
that the frequencies of the waves are restricted to the narrow
band used by Weber (1660 ± 0.03 Hz), the energy flux--integrated
over all wavelengths--must amount to about 10^6 J/m^2 (assuming that
the gravitational waves are distributed over a frequency interval
of several thousand hertz). Under the assumption that such

radiation is emitted uniformly in all spatial directions from the center of the galaxy we can compute the total energy E that is radiated by the galactic center during each event:

$$E = 4\pi A^2 \times 10^6 \ \text{J/m}^2 \approx 10^{47} \ \text{J} \tag{8.15}$$

where $A = 2 \times 10^{20}$ m is the distance of the earth to the galactic center. Corresponding to this energy is a mass $m = E/c^2 \approx 10M_\odot$! Since the initial experiments recorded several hundred events yearly (and since many signals remained undetected due to un-favorable detector position, statistical effects, etc.), we arrive at a yearly mass loss in our galaxy of $\approx 10^5 M_\odot$. This figure, how-ever, seemed to be totally unbelievable since within the (astro-physically short) time span of one million years our galaxy would have converted its entire mass into gravitational energy.

The exciting observations of Weber, as well as their almost unbelievable interpretations were discussed at numerous confer-ences. It was shown that the data analysis chosen by Weber was not optimal and, in fact, did not permit a unique interpretation of the measurements. A number of other gravitational wave anten-nas were built all over the world, with various improvements over Weber's first generation of detectors. So far, however, the ob-servations have not confirmed Weber's results. None of the other teams found any signs of gravitational waves having the intensity and occurring at the frequency observed by Weber.

Even though Weber's initial results have not found any con-firmation, his pioneering work has led to the development of increasingly sensitive gravitational wave receivers. The next generation of detectors will operate at a temperature of 4 K, thereby boosting the sensitivity by a factor of 1000-100,000. Looking further into the future, scientists hope to arrive at antennas operating at 3×10^{-3} K, resulting in an increase of sen-sitivity by a factor of 10^9 over Weber's detectors. Such antennas should be capable of receiving gravitational waves from the Virgo cluster of galaxies. According to theoretical estimates the gravitational radiation emitted during stellar collapses in this cluster should lead to several observable events per year.

Apart from these types of detectors, which all consist of modifications of Weber's concept, a totally different detector concept is currently being developed. It basically consists of a Michelson interferometer, which measures the slight distance variations between two points, caused by arriving gravitational waves. This new detector will provide a direct determination of the geometric space-time variations due to gravitational radiation. In order to reach the necessary accuracy of the interferometer, it will be necessary to construct a device measuring several kilometers in outer space.

CHAPTER 9

COSMOLOGY

Questions about the structure of the cosmos, its origin, and
its destination have puzzled mankind throughout history. Babylo-
nian and Greek philosophers and astronomers already tried to find
answers to these fundamental questions.

The quest for the structure of the universe also played an
important role in European cultural history. Historically, the
most significant step was the "Copernican revolution," which
finally laid to rest the belief that the earth forms the center of
the universe. This profound change in the perception of the cosmos was followed later by the realization that even the sun was
only one star among many, and during the nineteenth century astronomical progress led to increasingly detailed and meaningful questions about the structure of the universe.

Should we essentially equate the universe with our Milky Way,
floating lonely in the vast emptiness of space? Or are those
nebulous specks out there galaxies like our Milky Way, thus ex-
tending the domain of stars out into infinity? These questions
could only be resolved empirically around 1920 with the advent of
large telescopes. In the process a universe emerged, containing
countless galaxies beyond our own Milky Way, each galaxy in turn
being composed of about 100 billion stars.

This revelation of our scientific evolution has been called
the "cosmological principle," and will be discussed in the following section. Forming the foundation for relativistic cosmology,
the cosmological principle is one of the most fascinating

contributions of physics to the cultural history of our century. The knowledge that the universe is dynamically changing has led to entirely new ways of thinking.

THE COSMOLOGICAL PRINCIPLE

Any study of the universe as a whole must necessarily ignore local details, which would only confuse the picture. In order to arrive at a comprehensible theory, one has to find a simple model that will approximate the structures within the universe. The simplest model treats the distribution of matter throughout the universe as a uniform gas of constant density.

Of course, the matter in the universe is concentrated in stars, which in turn are clustered into galaxies. However, averaging over regions that are large compared to the distances between galaxies will lead to a gas or dust of uniform density. It turns out that within our observational limits this density is nearly constant (*homogeneous* universe), and independent of the direction in which we look (*isotropic* universe). This observational fact suggests that every point in the universe is equivalent to every other point; there are no preferred areas or directions in the cosmos. This assumption has been formulated as the cosmological principle that lies at the heart of relativistic cosmology:

> *The cosmological principle: the earth has no privileged*
> *place in the universe. In fact, the universe is homo-*
> *geneous and isotropic, i.e., it appears the same in any*
> *direction or from any spot.*

This simple assumption underlies all cosmological models. With the cosmological principle as our point of departure, we shall first construct cosmological models based on a Newtonian approximation. These models will then be modified in order to incorporate general relativity.

Problem 9.1: *The Cosmological Principle*

Think about the problem of experimentally verifying the cosmological principle. How could this be done and what difficulties would arise?

Problem 9.2: *Extraterrestrial Life*

When discussing the discovery of pulsars we mentioned the possibility of receiving signals from extraterrestrial civilizations. Can we deduce from the cosmological principle that life exists on other planetary systems, or would you dismiss this as an invalid extrapolation? In order to answer the question of extraterrestrial life, which scientific disciplines must be consulted, and what are some of the problems to be resolved?

THE INFINITE, HOMOGENEOUS, AND STATIC UNIVERSE

The cosmological principle invokes the picture of an infinite universe, which is uniformly and statically filled with stars. This model, however, leads to contradictions, which as early as 1800 were used as arguments against an infinite and eternal world. Where would all the energy come from to maintain the stars burning eternally? An infinite and static universe also would result in a night sky that would be as bright as the sun ("Olber's" paradox; see Fig. 9.1).

As is well known, the intensity of light reaching the earth from a star decreases proportionally to $1/r^2$, where r is the distance earth-star. On the other hand, the number of stars contained in a spherical shell with radii r and $r + dr$ increases with $r^2 dr$. Thus, the stars in this shell will contribute to the brightness of the night sky proportional to $(1/r^2)r^2 dr = dr$. Integration over all r from the nearest star (r_0) to $r = \infty$ yields

$$\int_{r_0}^{\infty} dr = \infty$$

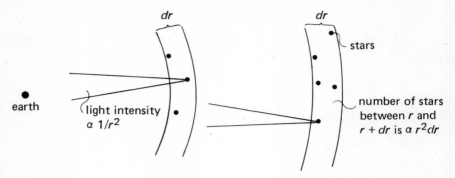

Fig. 9.1. Olber's paradox.

According to this argument, the total brightness of the sky would even be infinite! This deduction, however, is theoretically incorrect since the light of distant stars will be obscured by closer stars. The correct conclusion is: an infinite and eternal universe must be in thermal equilibrium, i.e., all bodies must eventually arrive at the same temperature. Thus, the earth would be heated by incoming radiation to several thousand degrees and would in turn radiate just as much as it receives. The sky would not know the difference between day and night. This "heat death" of a static and infinite universe is contrasted by the "cold death" of an "island" of stars. A lonely galaxy floating in an infinite and otherwise empty space will continuously radiate energy, eventually cooling down to absolute zero.

One further argument against the static, infinite universe follows from stability considerations: the slightest perturbation will cause such a world to expand or collapse.

Problem 9.3: Olber's Paradox

Would Olber's paradox still be a valid argument against an infinite and homogeneous universe if we assume that the stars only began to shine a few billion years ago?

COSMIC KINEMATICS: HUBBLE'S LAW AND THE
WORLD HORIZON

Our first attempt at creating a model of the universe must be
considered a failure. The infinite, static, homogeneous cosmos is
not a possible model of the world. Which of our assumptions must
be modified? Today, the impossibility of a static, infinite universe seems clear. The solar system can only have existed in its
current state for a few billion years, and lifetime of other stars
is about the same.

Mankind has always considered the sky of the "fixed" stars as
a symbol of "unchangeability," or "eternity." The recognition of
an "evolutionary universe" was therefore an enormously difficult
step, historically comparable to the step taken earlier by Darwin
in the field of biology.

The decisive fact was the discovery of the expansion of the
universe by Edwin Hubble in 1929. Hubble's measurements of the
red shift of spectral lines of distant galaxies, when interpreted
as a Doppler effect, exhibited a relationship in which galaxies
will recede from us with a velocity v directly proportional to
their distance x from earth:

$$v(t) = H(t)x(t) \tag{9.1}$$

This observation is sketched in Fig. 9.2. Allowing the proportionality factor $H(t)$ to be a function of time t enables us to
take into effect time-varying changes in the expansion of the
universe.

At first glance, Hubble's law (9.1) seems to suggest that the
earth stands at the center of the universe since all the galaxies
recede from us (as shown in Fig. 9.2). It is easy to demonstrate,
though, that given the expansion law (9.1), any arbitrary star
will form the apparent center of the expansion (or explosion).
Let

$$x(t) = y(t) + X(t) \tag{9.2}$$

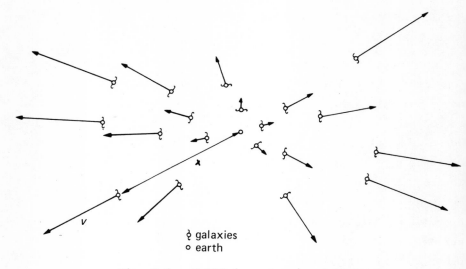

ç galaxies
o earth

Fig. 9.2. Hubble's expansion law.

where $X(t)$ is the coordinate of an arbitrary galaxy that moves
away from us with velocity

$$V(t) = H(t)X(t) \tag{9.3}$$

Then, with respect to that galaxy the velocity

$$v^{\prime}(t) = v(t) - V(t) \tag{9.4}$$

of the expansion will obey

$$v^{\prime}(t) = H(t)y(t) \tag{9.5}$$

as is seen by substituting (9.1), (9.2), and (9.3) into (9.4).
Equation (9.5) is Hubble's law again, and hence any galaxy in the
universe can consider itself as being the center of the expansion.
This is a very important fact since it implies that Hubble's law
(9.1) conforms to the cosmological principle. All that is known
about Hubble's function $H(t)$ is its value at the current time t_0:
$H_0 = H(t_0)$ is Hubble's constant. There is still considerable uncertainty about the numerical value of H_0. For many years, astronomers believed its value to be

$$H_0 = (55 \pm 7) \text{ km sec}^{-1} \text{ Mpc}^{-1} \qquad (9.6a)$$

but recent studies by D. Lynden-Bell at Cambridge have suggested a value

$$H_0 = (110 \pm 10) \text{ km sec}^{-1} \text{ Mpc}^{-1} \qquad (9.6b)$$

As we see, H_0 has the dimension of an inverse time. Using the value (9.6a), we find

$$H_0^{-1} = 1.8 \times 10^{10} \text{ years} \qquad (9.6c)$$

while (9.6b) yields

$$H_0^{-1} = 9 \times 10^9 \text{ years} \qquad (9.6d)$$

The value H_0^{-1} gives us an upper limit for the age of the universe as we shall see when we discuss the dynamics of the expansion.

Clearly, a determination of Hubble's constant H_0 is of fundamental importance to cosmology. During the almost 50 years since Hubble's discovery of the expansion of the universe, considerable efforts were made to obtain reliable data for H_0. The difficulties that arise are not caused by the red shift (and therefore velocity) measurements but rather by the uncertainty in the distance measurements needed in Eq. (9.1).

Figure 9.3 shows the data collected by Sandage in 1972. Plotted are the red shifts of the brightest galaxies contained in 84 clusters of galaxies. The reasoning goes as follows: assuming that the brightest galaxy in every cluster has about the same absolute magnitude (luminosity) as those observed in our neighboring clusters, we may deduce the distance from the apparent magnitude of each of those brightest galaxies. The distances would then lead us to a determination of Hubble's constant. Cosmic distance measurements are thus among the most important but also the most difficult tasks of cosmology.

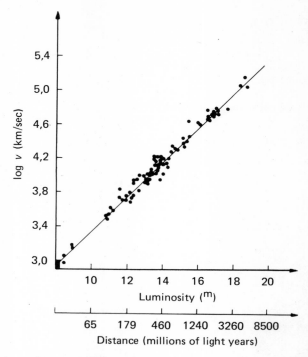

Fig. 9.3.   The red shift-distance relationship (Sandage, 1972).   The ordinate axis contains the logarithm of the escape velocity.   The abscissa contains the apparent luminosity (m = magnitude) of the brightest galaxies from 84 clusters, interpreted as distance from earth (in millions of light years).

In conclusion, we want to mention one further aspect of Hubble's law that has far-reaching consequences for the foundation and possibilities of cosmological research.   Since galaxies recede from us with a velocity directly proportional to their distance, there must be a point at which the velocity reaches and even exceeds the speed of light.   The set of all those points is called the *world horizon* (see Fig. 9.4).

According to Eq.(9.1), the distance $A = |x|$ to the world horizon is given by $c = HA$, or

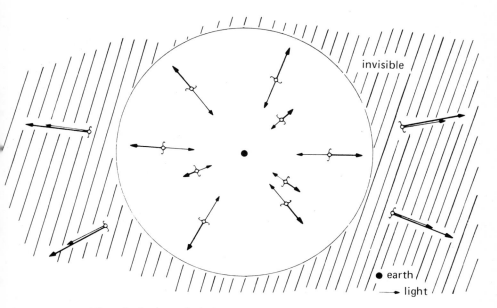

Fig. 9.4. Definition of the world horizon.

$A = c/H \approx 2 \times 10^{26}$ m $\approx 2 \times 10^{10}$ light years   (9.7)

assuming a value of $H_0 = 55$ km sec^{-1} Mpc^{-1}.

The closer a galaxy is to the world horizon, the larger is its Doppler red shift. According to $E = h\nu = hc/\lambda$, every photon loses energy due to the red shift, and therefore light from large distances arrives very weak. Finally, as a galaxy reaches the distance A, its red shift becomes infinite, and the energy of photons drops to zero, i.e.,

Galaxies that are located at or beyond the world horizon are invisible to us.

This situation is very reminiscent of that arising in the physics of black holes. There we met another horizon: the event horizon at the Schwarzschild radius. Light from within the event horizon of a black hole cannot escape because of the tremendous gravitational pull. Light from beyond the world horizon cannot reach us since the expansion happens so fast that the light is being "dragged along." Thus:

*Even if the universe were infinite, we could only perceive
a part of it that has a diameter of a few billion light
years.*

*Problem 9.4: Relativity Theory and Speeds Faster
            Than Light*

We just observed that galaxies beyond the horizon *A* recede
from us faster than the speed of light. How can this fact be re-
conciled with special relativity?

COSMIC DYNAMICS: EXPANSION AND BIG BANG

We can describe the motion of a randomly chosen galaxy through
its distance $x(t)$ from us by

$$x(t) \doteq R(t)x_0 \tag{9.8}$$

where $R(t)$ indicates the time-varying distance, while x_0 is the
initial position of the galaxy at an arbitrary point of time t_0.
Using Hubble's law (9.1), we obtain the following equation of
motion:

$$dR(t)/dt = H(t)R(t) \tag{9.9}$$

To this purely kinematic relation, we must add a dynamic equation
of motion, which incorporates the gravitational influence on the
motion of galaxies. A glance at Fig. 9.5 shows that the mass located between the earth and the galaxy will cause an acceleration
of that galaxy toward earth, thus slowing down the cosmic expansion. The equation of motion for the chosen galaxy is therefore

$$m\,\frac{dv}{dt} = -m\,\frac{GM(r)}{r^2}\,\frac{x}{r} \tag{9.10}$$

with

$$M(r) = \frac{4\pi}{3}\,\rho(t)r^3, \qquad r = |x|$$

mass outside the sphere does not contribute to the forces acting on the galaxy

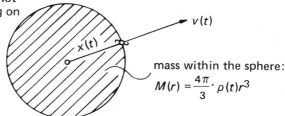

mass within the sphere:
$$M(r) = \frac{4\pi}{3} \cdot \rho(t) r^3$$

Fig. 9.5. Derivation of the fundamental equation of cosmology (Friedmann's equation).

Substitution of Eqs. (9.1) and (9.8) into (9.10), and observing that

$$v = HRx_0 = \frac{dR}{dt} x_0 \qquad (9.11)$$

yields the desired equation of motion for $R(t)$:

$$\frac{d^2 R}{dt^2} + \frac{4\pi}{3} G\rho(t) R = 0 \qquad (9.12)$$

Equation (9.12) contains two unknown functions $R(t)$ and $\rho(t)$ that must be found. The missing equation is provided by the assumption that the total mass in the universe is conserved. In formulas;

$$\rho(t) R^3(t) = \rho(t_0) R_0^3 \qquad (9.13)$$

Inserting (9.13) into Eq. (9.12) gives

$$2 \frac{d^2 R}{dt^2} + \frac{C}{R^2} = 0 \qquad (9.14)$$

the constant C being

$$C = \frac{8\pi G}{3} \rho(t_0) R_0^3 \qquad (9.15)$$

As usual, the equation of motion (9.14) leads to an energy law that expresses the conservation of energy during the motion:

$$\left(\frac{dR}{dt}\right)^2 - \frac{C}{R} + k = 0 \qquad\qquad (9.16)$$

If we differentiate (9.16) with respect to time, we indeed recover Eq.(9.14). Equation (9.16) is known as the *Friedmann equation*, and represents the fundamental equation of Newtonian cosmology. In fact, Friedmann's equation even holds unchanged in general relativity. The constant of integration k in (9.16) has the meaning of a negative energy density. In the general relativistic framework, however, this constant k will take on an entirely different meaning and, in fact, will be tied in with the curvature of space. The differential equation (9.16) can be solved easily by separating the variables. Writing

$$\frac{dR}{dt} = \left(\frac{C}{R} - k\right)^{1/2}$$

we obtain

$$\int_0^R \frac{dR´}{(C/R´ - k)^{1/2}} = \int dt = t \qquad\qquad (9.17)$$

The integral on the left can be found in every table of integrals, and depending on the sign of k, we find

$$\frac{kt}{C} = \frac{1}{2k^{1/2}} \text{ arc } \cos(1 - 2kR) - (R - kR^2)^{1/2}$$

$$\text{for } k > 0$$

$$\frac{t}{C} = \frac{2}{3}\left(\frac{R}{C}\right)^{3/2} \qquad\qquad \text{for } k = 0$$

$$\frac{|k|t}{C} = \left[\frac{R}{C} + |k|\left(\frac{R}{C}\right)^2\right]^{1/2}$$

$$- \frac{1}{2|k|^{1/2}} \text{ arc } \cos\left(\frac{2|k|R}{C} + 1\right) \qquad \text{for } k < 0 \qquad (9.18)$$

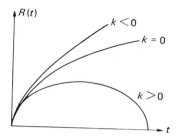

Fig. 9.6. Expansion of the universe for different values of k.

In Fig. 9.6 we have plotted the solutions (9.18) for the different values of k. Note that for small values of R (and therefore t) all three curves almost coincide. However, as R (and t) increases, the curves begin to exhibit significant differences: for $k > 0$ (negative energy), the distance between neighboring galaxies (which is proportional to R) increases for a while, reaches a maximum, and then decreases again until it becomes 0. This means that the initial explosion of the universe (the "big bang") did not have enough energy to sustain a continued expansion of the universe against the gravitational forces. Rather, the universe will expand, reach a maximum size, and then contract again. We shall see that this behavior will be equivalent to a "closed" universe in relativistic cosmology.

For $k = 0$ (total energy = 0) and $k < 0$ (positive total energy), the evolution of the universe is quite different. In both cases the expansion continues forever, never coming to a halt. Relativistic cosmology will equate this behavior with an "open," infinitely large universe.

The most significant result that follows from the dynamics of the universe is without question the explosive birth of the cosmos, known as the "big bang." Figure 9.6 shows that at time $t = 0$ the universe began as a primordial fireball of infinite density and infinitesimal size [$R(0) = 0$]. Knowledge of Hubble's constant H_0 allows us to estimate how much time has passed since the big bang, in other words, how old the universe is. If we denote this

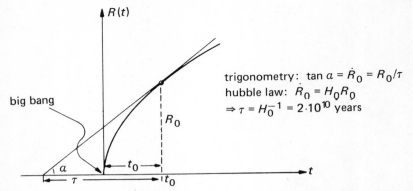

Fig. 9.7.   Interpretation of the Hubble constant.

current age of the universe by t_0, then a glance at Fig. 9.7 tells us that the so-called Hubble age $\tau = H_0^{-1}$ must be somewhat greater than the actual age t_0. Assuming the value $H_0^{-1} = 2 \times 10^{10}$ years, we can estimate:

Age of universe: $t_0 \approx 7 - 15$ *billion years*

We shall return to a discussion of the tremendous uncertainty in the value of t_0 when we deal with the question of whether the universe is "open" or "closed."

Problem 9.5:   Newtonian Cosmology

Is our derivation of Eq. (9.12) really valid?   What assumption were tacitly made?

Problem 9.6:   The Early Universe

Show that for small values of t (early universe), the three expansion laws (9.18) all lead to the same equation,

$$R = C(3t/2C)^{2/3}$$

Thus, in the early stages the expansion is independent of the spatial curvature k.   Why?

GEOMETRY OF THE UNIVERSE: THE CURVATURE OF SPACE

So far, we have based our cosmological models entirely on Newton's physics. As it turns out, if we would develop the dynamics of the cosmos based on Einstein's gravitational field equations, we would obtain the same relationship between mass density and expansion [Eq.(9.16)]. The difference is that the constant k takes on a new meaning in relativistic cosmology: it describes the curvature of the universe. In order to clarify this remark, we must first talk about *spaces of constant curvature*.

The point of departure of our cosmological studies has been the cosmological principle, which postulates the equivalence of all points and directions in the universe: ignoring local irregularities, the universe looks the same from every point. If we intend to dtudy the large-scale (global) geometry of the universe, then we must again be guided by the cosmological principle.

In order to provide a clear and intuitive treatment, we shall proceed analogous to our discussion of measuring sticks in Chapter 3. Figure 9.8 shows an astronomer who scans the universe and observes all those stars and galaxies that are located in the same plane. Ignoring local details (like the earth), this plane divides the universe into two identical parts.

The situation is analogous to that of the cross-sectional plane through the sun (Chapter 3). Just as we did then, we can

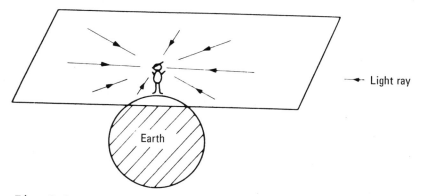

Fig. 9.8. An astronomer views the universe along a plane.

now pose the question of which geometry prevails on that surface
if we attempt to survey it with measuring sticks. In order to
gain some intuitive insight into this geometry we shall—just as
we did in Chapter 3—construct a model surface exhibiting the same
geometrical behavior as the "cosmic slice" of Fig. 9.8. The cosmological principle will help us to reduce the multitude of theoretical possibilities to a few simple alternative models.

Suppose a group of astronomers from different galaxies per-
forms the same experiment as our earthbound observer. Clearly,
according to the cosmological principle they must all arrive at
the same model of the geometry governing "their" observational
surfaces. After all, the universe must look the same from every
galaxy!

Obviously, our conclusion would hold for the plane shown in
Fig. 9.9, but not for the rounded cone of Fig. 9.10, since the
galaxy located at the tip of the cone would have a preferred
status not shared by the other galaxies.

Are there any other geometrical configurations besides the
plane that are compatible with the cosmological principle? Such a
surface must clearly have a curvature that is the same at all
points and in all directions. Mathematicians have classified such
surfaces of constant curvatures in full generality. Next to the
plane of Fig. 9.9, the spherical surface of Fig. 9.11 is the simplest non-Euclidean surface that obeys the cosmological principle.

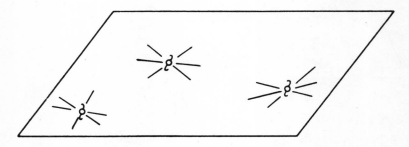

*Fig. 9.9. A plane is a possible model for the cosmic cross-
sectional surface since all its points are equivalent.*

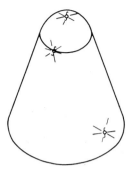

Fig. 9.10. The cross section cannot be a conical surface since the tip (here shown as rounded) of the cone would occupy a unique position, contradicting the cosmological principle.

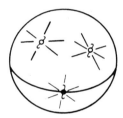

Fig. 9.11. A spherical surface does not contradict the cosmological principle: all its points (galaxies) are equivalent.

Having found two surface models that satisfy the cosmological principle, we must next address the problem of how to experimentally decide between the two possibilities: plane or sphere? The basic idea is illustrated in Fig. 9.12.

Let us imagine that the galaxies are regularly distributed throughout the universe, and let a be the (constant) distance between any two neighboring galaxies. If the slice through the universe has the configuration of a plane (Fig. 9.9), then we should find approximately six galaxies located at distance a from us (we have approximated $2\pi \approx 6$). On the other hand, if we are dealing with a spherical surface, we should expect to find less galaxies at distance a than on a plane surface. These remarks suggest that we replace the surveying of the surface with measuring sticks

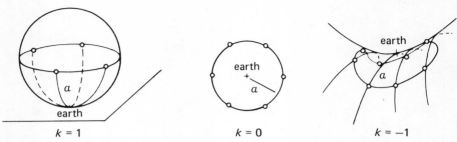

$$k = 1 \qquad\qquad k = 0 \qquad\qquad k = -1$$

Fig. 9.12.   Distribution of galaxies in the universe.

(which is impossible at a cosmic scale, anyway) by a galaxy count
as a function of distance.   The approximately constant distance
between neighboring galaxies will provide a natural distance scale
for us!

Figure 9.12 shows the three basic types of surfaces of constant curvature: we already know the spherical surface of constant positive curvature and the Euclidean plane of zero curvature.   The third type is a surface of constant negative curvature.
Its existence is not quite as intuitive as that of the first two
types.   However, mathematics has shown that such a surface of constant negative curvature exists (in the mathematical sense), and
for such a "saddle" surface the galaxy count as a function of distance increases faster than for the plane.

Let us now return from two-dimensional cross-sectional surfaces to three-dimensional space.   A space whose cut surfaces are
all planes is a Euclidean space.   If the cross sections have the
geometry of spheres, then we are dealing with a closed spherical
cosmos.   The third possibility, finally, is the open, infinite
hyperbolic universe, whose cross sections all have the geometry of
saddle surfaces.

The suggestion that the universe might have a non-Euclidean
geometry was one of the most revolutionary achievements of general
relativity.   The spherical universe, described by Einsteing in his
famous "Cosmological Considerations to the General Theory of Relativity" (1917) for the first time confronted mankind with the

possibility of a closed, finite, and yet unbounded cosmos. In
this universe, all (optically flat) cross-sectional surfaces are
spheres. A traveler (or light ray) moving in a "straight" direction will return to the point of departure after a finite amount
of time! The spherical universe has a finite volume and contains
a finite number of galaxies.

Problem 9.7: Models of the Universe

The three surfaces depicted in Fig. 9.12 can be considered
either as cross sections through the universe (as we did), or as
two-dimensional *models* of the universe, as is done in many popular
books. Discuss the didactic advantages and disadvantages of both
interpretations.

DECISION BETWEEN UNIVERSES: FINITE OR INFINITE?

The arguments presented in the previous section have shown
that the cosmological principle admits only three fundamentally
different geometries for the universe: Euclidean, spherical, or
hyperbolic space. We also saw that a decision between these al-
ternatives can be made by counting the number of galaxies as a
function of their distance from us: if the number-count increases
with r^2, the universe is Euclidean, a smaller increase points to a
spherical, a faster increase to a hyperbolic world.

Unfortunately, such a direct experimental decision is currently not feasible, the reason being an effect that we have not
yet taken into account: looking into the vast distances of space
also means looking into the past! The further away a galaxy is
located from us, the longer its light had to travel before reaching earth. Due to the expansion, the curvature of the universe
was different in the past than it is today (compare Fig. 9.13).
This effect, however, can be taken into consideration without much
trouble, and does not cause any qualitative changes in the results
obtained from galaxy counts.

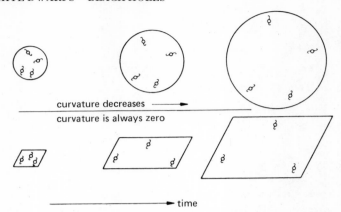

curvature decreases ──────▶

curvature is always zero

──────────────────────▶ time

Fig. 9.13. Evolution of the cosmic curvature as a result of the expansion (for simplicity, we only show the Euclidean and the spherical universe).

It is another effect that is of importance, but evades quantitative analysis. We are talking about the changes in the luminosity of galaxies during the eons of cosmic evolution. If we should perceive more galaxies at large distances than would correspond to an r^2 increase, could that fact perhaps be explained as a higher luminosity of past galaxies? According to this explanation, smaller galaxies could be visible, thereby upsetting the statistics. As long as we have no knowledge about this effect, we cannot use galaxy counts to draw conclusions about the finiteness or infinity of the universe.

Another approach might help in deciding among the different cosmological models: the study of the corrections to the red shift-distance relationship. These corrections arise as follows: in a closed spherical world, each galaxy has fewer "neighbors" than in a Euclidean world. Hence, each neighboring galaxy will receive somewhat more light and will therefore appear slightly brighter than would be expected from its distance. Since the distance estimation of galaxies is based on their luminosity, a spherical universe will lead to an underestimation of distances, while a hyperbolic universe will cause an overestimation. The

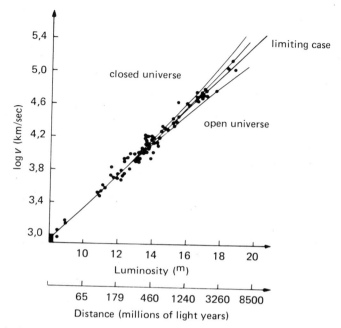

Fig. 9.14. The corrections to the red shift-distance relationship for different universes.

resulting corrections to the Hubble diagram are shown in Fig. 9.14 together with experimental data.

The observational data seem to hint at a closed universe. However, even here we must allow for evolutionary effects, which render impossible the determination of the curvature of the universe: a time-varying change in the luminosity of galaxies can lead to deviations from Hubble's law. Assuming that galaxies used to be brighter in the past, we would have overestimated their distance, an effect that we earlier blamed on the curvature of space. Both attempts--galaxy count and red shift corrections--must for now be considered inconclusive, since *evolutionary effects and curvature effects are currently indistinguishable.* What is needed is much better knowledge about the evolution of galaxies, before we can make any progress (compare Chapter 10).

A third attempt to decide between an open or closed universe establishes the connection with the dynamics of the universe that we discussed earlier. Friedmann's Eq.(9.16), describing the expansion of the universe, contains the radius $R(t)$ and the parameter k. In relativistic cosmology, Friedmann's equation is still valid but $R(t)$ and k assume new geometric meaning. Due to the fixed (Euclidean) structure of space in Newton's theory, these terms did not have any geometric significance. Table 9.1 summarizes the geometric meaning of R and k. The diagrams on the

TABLE 9.1.

Geometry of the universe	k	R(t)
Spherical (closed) World	1	$R(t)$ is the radius of the universe, i.e., of the spherical slices
Euclidean (infinite) World	0	$R(t)$ is a mean distance between galaxies
Hyperbolic (infinite) World	-1	$R(t)$ is the curvature radius of the universe

right-hand side of the table indicate the behavior of the "world radius" $R(t)$ as obtained from (9.16).

For $k = 1$ we have a closed, finite universe, which was born about 10-15 billion years ago in a "big bang" ($R = 0$). The expansion is slowing down, and after reaching a maximal size, the universe begins to collapse again.

The case $k = 0$ corresponds to an open, infinite universe, which began with a big bang and will expand forever. The geometry is Euclidean.

Finally, if $k = -1$, we are dealing with an open, infinite hyperbolic universe. It began with a big bang, which was violent enough to allow the expansion to continue forever against the existing gravitational forces. The situation is the same as for $k = 0$, except that the geometry is hyperbolic instead of Euclidean.

We can distinguish the three cases by applying one simple physical idea: the deceleration of the expansion is caused by the total gravitational attraction in the universe. Only a sufficiently large mean mass density will bring the expansion to an eventual halt, followed by a contraction of the universe. Thus, *a closed and finite universe can exist only if the mass density has a certain minimal value.*

In order to derive this minimal density, we divide the Friedmann Eq.(9.16) by R^2:

$$\frac{\dot{R}^2}{R^2} - \frac{8\pi G}{3}\frac{\rho(t_0)R_0^3}{R^3} = -\frac{k}{R^2} \tag{9.19}$$

Next we substitute $R = R_0$, i.e., we specialize the equation to the current state of the universe. Using $H_0 = \dot{R}_0/R_0$, we obtain

$$H_0^2 - \frac{8\pi G}{3}\rho(t_0) = -\frac{k}{R_0^2} \tag{9.20}$$

The universe will be closed (finite) if

$$H_0^2 < \frac{8\pi G}{3}\rho(t_0) \tag{9.21}$$

since $k = 1$ (closed universe) implies that the left-hand side of (9.20) is negative. The minimal density required for a closed universe is given by

$$\rho(t_0) > \frac{3}{8\pi G} H_0^{\ 2} \tag{9.22}$$

Substituting the value (9.6a) for Hubble's constant H_0, we find

$$\rho(t_0) > 5 \times 10^{-27} \text{ kg/m}^3 \tag{9.23}$$

However, observations seem to indicate a mean density of the universe of

$$\rho(t_0) \approx 3 \times 10^{-28} \text{ kg/m}^3 \tag{9.24}$$

This observed value does not satisfy (9.23), thereby suggesting an open universe. Unfortunately, the value given in (9.24) is by no means guaranteed since large amounts of invisible interstellar matter (including black holes) could significantly increase the value of $\rho(t_0)$. Of course, a closed universe would require an increase in the density (9.24) by a factor of 20-100. Whether or not that much invisible matter exists is not known today.

The question about the large-scale structure of the cosmos is therefore still unsolved: a finite or infinite universe--we are still awaiting a decision.

CHAPTER 10

COSMOGONY AND THE EARLY UNIVERSE

In Chapter 4 we took a systematic look at the structures that occur in the cosmos: planets and moons, stars, stellar clusters, galaxies, and clusters of galaxies. Using a relatively simple theory we were able to explain the typical sizes of planets, main sequence stars, white dwarfs, and neutron stars. The fact that the typical mass of a normal star is roughly comparable to the solar mass was another result. Yet certain questions remained unanswered: What determines the mass of a galaxy? How did the cosmic structures (like the solar system) evolve? Can we explain the chemical composition of stars?

These, and many other related questions belong to the field of *cosmogony*, which is the study of the evolution of cosmic structures. In this chapter we intend to study a few selected fundamental problems of cosmogony, concentrating on the theory of the early universe. Here, the term "early universe" refers to the first seconds, hours, years, and millions of years—but not *billions* of years—following the big bang creation of our world. Perhaps, most surprising is the fact that meaningful physical statements concerning this early phase are at all possible. As has happened so frequently in the history of science, this fact is also the result of a lucky accident.

THE DISCOVERY OF THE COSMIC BACKGROUND RADIATION

In 1965 two American scientists, Penzias and Wilson, acci-
dentally came across a discovery that had a tremendous impact on
the further development of cosmology and cosmogony. While trying
to monitor signals from satellites, they detected electromagnetic
radiation that seemed to arrive on earth isotropically from all
directions and therefore could not be pinpointed to any particular
source in the universe. During the next few years, studies were
conducted to determine the spectral distribution of that radiation, resulting in the discovery that it was a thermal radiation
with a temperature of 2.7°K (Figs. 10.1 and 10.2).

Twenty years earlier, Gamov and his colleagues had already
predicted the existence of such a radiation: the cosmic background radiation. They had postulated that right after the big
bang, the universe must have been extremely hot, and that intense
nuclear reactions must have taken place during this early phase.
Gamov suspected that these reactions contributed to the creation

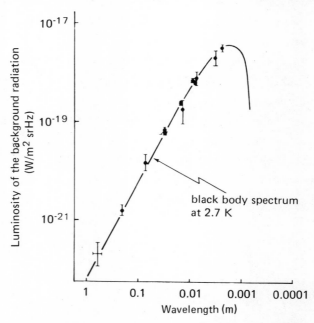

Fig. 10.1. Spectrum of the cosmic background radiation.

Fig. 10.2.   R. Wilson and A. Penzias in front of the horn an-
tenna that led to the discovery of the cosmic background radiation
(1965).

of some of the chemical elements. Based on this theory, R. M.
Dicke of Princeton University was actively trying to detect rem-
nants of the cosmic background radiation, when along came the discovery of Penzias and Wilson.

COSMIC RADIATION

There is a characteristic distinction between the behavior of
radiation and of matter in the universe. For matter we have the
conservation law [Eq.(9.13)]; for radiation we must derive a separate set of laws.

Let us consider a photon being emitted by a galaxy at time t_1
and received on earth at time t_0. The situation is depicted in
Fig. 10.3, with the galaxy being at the origin of the coordinate
system, and the earth moving away at a speed $v = Hr_0$ (Hubble's

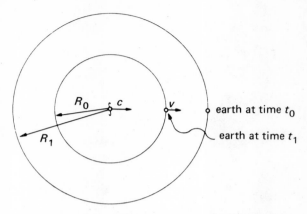

Fig. 10.3. Derivation of the characteristics of cosmic radiation.

law). If λ_1 is the photon's wavelength at the time t_1 of its emission, then at the time t_0 of its arrival on earth its wavelength λ_0 will be

$$\lambda_0 = \left(1 + \frac{v}{c}\right)\lambda_1 \tag{10.1}$$

Also, while the photon is traveling, the radius of the universe increases according to

$$\frac{R_0}{R_1} = \frac{r_0}{r} = \frac{c}{c - v} \approx 1 + \frac{v}{c} = \frac{\lambda_0}{\lambda_1} \tag{10.2}$$

The expansion of the universe causes a red shift for which the wavelength is proportional to the universe's radius. For example, should the universe double in radius during the time between emission and reception of the radiation, then every light quantum (photon) will also double its wavelength. (Note that our derivation is only valid for $v/c \ll 1$, i.e., $\lambda_0/\lambda_1 \approx 1$. However, it can be shown rigorously that our result remains valid for *arbitrary* velocities and red shifts.) Now a light quantum of double wavelength (i.e., half the frequency) has only half its original energy. Consequently, as the universe expands, the total energy of electromagnetic radiation in the universe decreases inversely proportional to the radius of the universe:

$$E_{rad} \propto 1/R \tag{10.3}$$

The radiation energy and the radiation density ρ_R are connected according to

$$E_{rad} = \rho_R \frac{4\pi}{3} R^3 \tag{10.4}$$

Thus, for electromagnetic radiation

$$\rho_R(t) R^4(t) = \rho_R(t_0) R^4(t_0) \tag{10.5}$$

The density of electromagnetic radiation decreases faster than the (mass-) density of matter!

Using the Stefan-Boltzmann law we can deduce the energy density w and thus the mass density ρ_R of radiation from its temperature:

$$\rho_R = \frac{w}{c^2} = \left(\frac{4\sigma}{c^3} \right) T^4 \tag{10.6}$$

Here,

$$\sigma = 2\pi^5 k^4 / 15 h^3 c^2$$

is the Stefan-Boltzmann constant; its numerical value is $\sigma = 5.67 \times 10^{-8}$ W/m^{2}K^4. Setting $T = 2.7$ K, we obtain

$$\rho_R(t_0) = 4.5 \times 10^{-31} \text{ kg/m}^3 \tag{10.7}$$

Currently, ρ_R is negligible against the density of matter in the universe. However, as we go back in time we should reach a point at which the radiation density (which increases faster as the universe becomes smaller) will surpass the matter density. The universe, as it existed before that point in time, will have been *dominated by radiation*. Using the conservation laws (9.13) and

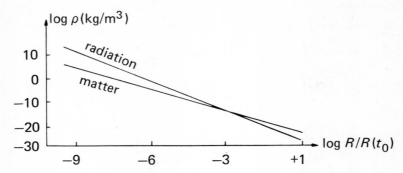

Fig. 10.4. Radiation density vs. matter density in the universe.

(10.5) we can say that this point in time was reached when the universe was roughly 1000 times smaller than today (see Fig. 10.4).

From the dynamic behavior of the universe (Friedmann equation) we can estimate the duration of the early phase of the universe (in which radiation was dominant) to about one million years (compare Problem 10.1).

Problem 10.1: Duration of the Early Universe

In order to derive the Friedmann Eq. (9.16), we made use of the conservation law (9.13). Since (9.13) is only valid for matter, we are not allowed to apply Eq. (9.16) for the early universe. Instead, the expansion law for the early phase of the cosmos must be based on Eq. (9.12) together with

$$\rho(t) = \rho_R(t_0)\,(R_0/R)^4$$

Show that the resulting Friedmann equation is given by

$$\left(\frac{dR}{dt}\right)^2 - \frac{A^2}{R^2} + k = 0 \tag{10.8}$$

with $A^2 = 2\pi G \rho_R(t_0) R_0^4/3$. Integrate Eq. (10.8) and neglect k against A^2/R^2 (since R is small). Show that

$$R/R_0 = (t/t_R)^{1/2}$$

(10.9)

with

$$t_R = \left[\frac{8\pi}{3} G\rho_R(t_0) \right]^{-1/2}$$

(10.10)

Compute t_R, and from that deduce the duration of the early universe by using $R/R_0 = 10^{-3}$ as the end of the radiation-dominated period (Fig. 10.4).

THE EARLY UNIVERSE

How can we visualize the first million years of the evolution of the universe? What does it mean to say that the world was dominated by radiation?

An answer to these questions must take into consideration the fact that the radiation in the young universe was not only much denser but also much hotter than it is today. Since the radiation density obeys the two relations

$$\rho \propto T^4 , \qquad \rho \propto R^{-4}$$

(10.11)

the temperature must be inversely proportional to the radius R of the universe:

$$T = 2.7 \text{ K} \times (R_0/R)$$

(10.12)

As we trace the history of the universe from its birth (big bang), we can distinguish several epochs that are characterized by the radiation temperature. These phases are summarized in Table 10.1.

During the first 10^{-4} sec after the big bang the temperature was so high that the elementary particles in the universe (protons, neutrons, etc.) reached relativistic speeds and constantly collided at high energies, forming new particles, which, however, annihilated themselves almost immediately. This chaotic epoch saw

TABLE 10.1.

Time	Radius	Density (kg/m^3)	Temperature (K)
10^{17} years	10^{26} m	10^{-27}	3
	Era of the stars		
10^6 years	10^{23} m	10^{-18}	10^4
	Era of radiation		
1000 sec	10^{17} m	1	10^8
	Era of nuclear reactions		
10^{-4} sec	10^{14} m	10^{18}	10^{12}
	Era of hadrons		

an equilibrium of creation and annihilation of matter and anti-matter. Following these first 10^{-4} sec the temperature in the universe sank sufficiently for protons and neutrons to slow down to nonrelativistic speeds. Under these conditions the creation of antiparticles was no longer possible. However, the temperature was still higher than several billions of degrees, thus causing highly intense nuclear reactions to take place. This age of nuclear reactions lasted for about 1000 sec after the big bang, and at its end the temperature had sunk to about 100 million degrees Kelvin.

During the age of the hadrons (i.e., the first 10^{-4} sec) one cannot yet speak of chemical elements. On the other hand, during the next phase, the age of the nuclear reactions, individual atomic nuclei begin to form, and it is possible to follow the creation of the chemical elements. Figure 10.5 shows the creation of helium and deuterium shortly after the big bang. As a matter of fact, these light elements are the only two that existed in the first few seconds of the universe. All the heavier elements must

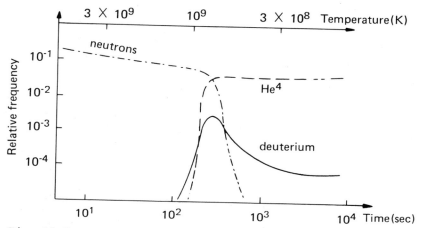

Fig. 10.5. Formation of the elements after the big bang.

have been created much later by nuclear processes that took place in stars or in supernova explosions.

The third epoch listed in Table 10.1 is the age of radiation. During that period, which lasted for several million years after the birth of the universe, the radiation density dominated over the mass density. The temperature during that period was still relatively high (above 10,000 K), and matter existed in the form of a highly ionized plasma.

During the following period, the age of the stars, matter began to condense into stars, which in turn clustered into galaxies. This process of the creation of discrete structures is the topic of the next two sections.

THE FORMATION OF STRUCTURES

In the last section of Chapter 4 we tried to provide a systematic summary of the structures that can be found in the universe. We saw then that in selected cases it was possible to deduce certain properties of objects from their atomic structure: thus we were able to derive the mass-radius relationship for moons, planets, white dwarfs, and neutron stars shown in Fig. 4.13.

There is another question, though, that cannot be answered by studying the atomic composition. This question concerns the *frequency* with which different objects occur in the universe. Why are white dwarfs so numerous in our galaxy? How many neutron stars exist?

Even the most fundamental properties of stellar clusters and galaxies cannot be explained through their composition: What determines the size of a galaxy? Why do globular clusters contain about 10^6 stars?

These types of questions cannot be resolved by looking at the *structure* but only by concentrating on the *history* of the object under consideration. Understanding the history is the task of cosmogony.

In the previous sections we used cosmogony to sketch the early evolution of the universe. Now we intend to use it in order to understand the formation of the structures within the universe.

Let us begin by studying the frequency distribution of the elements in the cosmos (Fig. 10.6). How did this distribution come about? In the previous section we already obtained a partial answer: light elements, primarily helium, were presumably formed in the first hour of the universe. Calculations show, however, that heavier elements cannot be created in the same manner.

The reason lies in the nonexistence of stable elements with mass numbers 5 and 8. None of the possible reactions involving H and He, or He and He will produce heavier elements. The understanding of the formation of the heavier elements seemed to have come up against an impenetrable wall. A breakthrough was achieved in 1952 by Edwin Salpeter, who demonstrated that the beryllium nucleus Be^8 that results from the reaction $He^4 + He^4 \rightarrow Be^8$ exists for only 10^{-16} sec, but long enough to guarantee a continuous production of a small number of Be nuclei in a star. The reaction $3He^4 \rightarrow Be^8 + He^4 \rightarrow C^{12}$ generates a carbon nucleus, and thus provides a basis for the formation of heavier elements through fusion reactions. In the interior of stars reactions like $C^{12} + He^4 \rightarrow O^{16}$

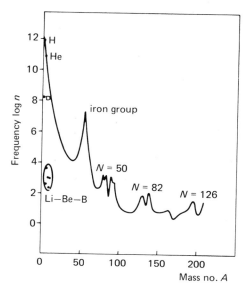

Fig. 10.6.   Frequency distribution of the chemical elements.

and O^{16} + He^4 → Ne^{20}, taking place at temperatures of a few 100 million degrees Kelvin will build atomic nuclei up to mass numbers of about 40.   Figure 10.6 shows a drop in the frequency curve in this regime.   This drop is due to the fact that with increasing charge more and more energy is required to penetrate the Coulomb barrier of the nucleus during fusion.

Another interesting feature of the curve in Fig. 10.6 is the strong maximum for iron.   This can also be explained qualitatively: iron has the highest binding energy per nucleon (i.e., the iron nucleus is held together more strongly than any other nucleus). Consequently, neither fusion nor fission of iron nuclei will produce energy.   Only by investing energy can an iron nucleus be transformed into other chemical elements.

Let us also mention how to explain the large frequency oscillations for other heavy elements.   The typical nuclear reactions that take place in stars are unable to produce the heavy elements. The necessary temperatures would cause any star to become unstable

(due to the radiation pressure), presumably resulting in a supernova explosion. The origin of the heavy elements can probably be
found in these violent catastrophes. Through neutron capture,
nuclei of higher and higher mass are built. The change of the
concentration N_A of atomic nuclei with atomic weight A is proportional to

$$dN_A \propto -\sigma_A N_A + \sigma_{A-1} N_{A-1} \qquad (10.13)$$

where σ_A is the cross section of the atomic nucleus A for neutron
capture. Since the capture of neutrons by A leads to nuclei with
mass numbers $A + 1$, the term $\sigma_A N_A$ in Eq.(10.13) has a negative
sign (the concentration of A is diminished), while neutron capture
of nuclei with mass number $A - 1$ and concentration N_{A-1} will lead
to an increase in the concentration of nuclei of mass number A.
Equilibrium exists if $dN_A = 0$, i.e.,

$$\sigma_A N_A = \sigma_{A-1} N_{A-1} \qquad (10.14)$$

Thus, the product of the neutron capture cross section σ_A with the
relative frequency N_A should be a constant independent of A. Approximately, this is indeed the case. We may therefore suspect
that the process of neutron capture is responsible for the creation and frequency distribution of the heavy elements.

Having presented a rough outline of the creation of the chemical elements we shall now turn to the formation of stars. The
basic theory had already been sketched in the first section of
Chapter 4, and in Problems 4.2 and 4.3. Let us summarize the
facts: the Jeans criterion [Eq.(4.17)] says that masses

$$M \gtrsim \left(\frac{kT}{G\mu}\right)^{3/2} \frac{1}{\sqrt{\rho}} \qquad (10.15)$$

will become unstable due to their own gravitational weight. The
density and temperature of the interstellar gas causes the contraction of gas clouds of several thousand solar masses. As the
density of the contracting cloud rises (and before any noticeable

increase in temperature), the unstable mass decreases according to Eq.(10.15) and subclouds of a few solar masses begin to form the first stars. These initial stars heat up the remaining gas to about 10^4 K, and clouds of ionized hydrogen gas (HII clouds) result. Due to the increased temperature in those HII regions the pressure rises, causing these regions to expand, thereby squeezing the nonionized hydrogen clouds into "globules." The globules eventually become new stars. The numerical computation of these general ideas has progressed far enough to consider the theory of star formation as basically understood.

There are also attempts to explain the formation of spherical stellar clusters, also called "globular" clusters. These clusters, consisting of about one million stars and being about ten billion years old are sprinkled around our galaxy. In contrast to the other stars their location is not restricted to the galactic plane. How did these clusters develop and why do they contain about 10^6 stars? The great age of the stars in those clusters suggests that they must have formed during the early phases of the universe.

According to Table 10.1, at the beginning of the epoch of the stars--one million years after the big bang--the density in the universe had dropped to 10^{-18} kg/m^3 and the temperature was about 10^4 K. If we substitute these values into Eq.(10.15) we see that during that time period masses of the order of $M \gtrsim 10^6 M_\odot$ were unstable. We have here at least one first clue that might explain the mass and age of globular clusters.

The formation of galaxies and clusters of galaxies, on the other hand, is a complex problem that in recent years has given rise to numerous different hypotheses. So far no theory has been found that could explain all of the observational data (like mass, angular momentum) in a satisfactory manner from cosmological considerations.

In this book we can only present a highly general qualitative picture: about 10 billion years ago our galaxy developed out of a nearly spherical turbulent gas cloud. A small fraction of this

cloud condensed into smaller clouds that eventually evolved into
stellar clusters. Gradually, the gas cloud contracted. The initial angular momentum caused a flattening of the spherical cloud
into a disk-shaped structure. This model can also explain the
velocity distribution of the stars in the galaxy, as well as the
existence of a galactic nucleus and the spiral structure. The
questions that remain unanswered concern our initial assumptions:
Why do gas clouds of $10^{11} M_\odot$ contract? What determines their angular momentum?

ACCIDENT OR NECESSITY: SOLAR SYSTEM AND LIFE

The results of the previous sections are actually quite remarkable: the history of the universe is characterized by the
fact that an initial homogeneous and hot hydrogen gas converted
itself into a multiple of complex structures like atomic nuclei,
stars, and galaxies. This process is really directly opposed to
our normal experience. Typically, thermodynamic processes do not
lead to the integration but to the disintegration of structures:
gases tend to fill their container uniformly, temperature differences will be equalized through heat diffusion, oscillations are
damped, and any motion will eventually come to a halt due to friction. *Does the evolution of the universe with its constant formation of new structures contradict the laws of thermodynamics?*
Clearly, this cannot be the case since all our discussions were
based on thermodynamic arguments. In fact, in recent years
scientists--particularly the Belgian school around Prigogine--
have begun to analyze the conditions under which dissipative (i.e.
entropy-increasing) processes actually create rather than destroy
structures. Manfred Eigen (nobel laureate for chemistry) has
tried to apply this theory to the *development of life,* by showing
that the phenomena of life can be reduced to "self-organization"
of matter, and thus form the culmination in our previously discussed chain of spontaneous creations of structures. On the other
hand, Jacques Monod in his famous study on accident or necessity

has tried to argue that life is something extremely improbable. The fact that there is even one planet with life in the entire universe is the result of an enormously lucky coincidence. According to Monod a totally lifeless universe would have been much more probable--a world that expands and eventually contracts for nobody; in which stars are born and die, observed by no one; a gigantic "cosmic machine" that, once put into motion, proceeds according to its own laws and yet without any goal. Sad.

Is life really restricted to earth? Does life occur only in one spot of a universe that contains 10^{22} stars and has a size of billions of light years? Or is it possible that there are other civilizations "out there," just waiting to establish contact with us, or perhaps already actively trying to reach us? What are some of the problems to be solved, and what kinds of experiments do we have to perform before we can even attempt to scientifically approach such questions?

Here, we shall deal with only one aspect that relates closely to our earlier discussion: life can only develop on planets with suitable conditions of temperature and atmospheric consistency. Yet, how many stars are surrounded by planets? Is the formation of a planetary system an accident or an almost necessary by-product of the contraction of a gas cloud to a star?

In the case of our own solar system the theory of its genesis has widely oscillated between both points of view. Following the initial work of Descartes, Kant and Laplace attempted to explain the evolution of the solar system in a manner that was very reminiscent of our earlier model of the galaxy formation: a gas cloud contracts, accelerating its rotation, and gradually dissolves into subclouds, which eventually contract to become planets. Later, Henri Poincaré tried to formulate this theory mathematically with partial success. One problem remained unsolved: Why does the sun rotate so slowly? During the contraction of a primeval gas cloud its innermost part ought to rotate much faster than is observed for the sun.

Consequently, around 1900 the Swedish physicist and chemist Arrhenius suggested an alternative theory: a collision took place between the sun and another star. The resulting tidal forces caused parts of the solar matter to be expelled into space. Several billion years ago this expelled matter formed into the planets. This theory was adopted and worked out in detail by Jeans, and successfully solved the problem of the slow rotation of the sun.

Yet collisions between stars are quite rare, and during the entire lifetime of the universe very few such catastrophes have occurred. Hence, the theory of Arrhenius and Jeans would consider the creation of planetary systems a highly improbable *accident,* while according to Kant and Laplace planets would *necessarily* accompany stellar formation.

In the meantime theory and observational evidence have decided in favor of Kant and Laplace. Their theory was improved and perfected by Weizsäcker, Lüst, and others. The puzzle concerning the slow solar rotation became at least qualitatively understandable after the discovery of the "solar wind." Despite a number of unanswered questions, this theory is probably a fairly correct model of the genesis of our solar system.

The "collision-hypothesis" of Arrhenius is also refuted by observations: detailed measurements of the orbital motion of Barnard's star suggest strongly that this star is being orbited by at least one planet. Barnard's star, however, is only six light years away from us, and thus one of our nearest "neighbors." If two such neighboring stars possess planetary systems then it is quite improbable that such systems are the result of such rare occurrences as stellar collisions.

Everything seems to indicate that the existence of planets—clearly a necessary condition for the development of life—is quite common in the universe. In fact, there are estimates suggesting that between 1 and 10% of all stars in the universe are surrounded by planetary systems (i.e., 10^{20} to 10^{21} of all 10^{22}

stars within the visible universe might have planets). How many
of those planets actually sustain life? Is this extraterrestrial
life also based on carbon-hydrogen compounds as on earth? Many
speculations surround these and similar questions, and in recent
years some experiments have even been initiated. The calculations
done by Eigen are first attempts to obtain quantitative results
from qualitative hypotheses.

Can we possibly decide empirically whether other planets carry
life, or whether there is even intelligent life in the universe,
extraterrestrial civilizations with which contact might be established? Until a few years ago, these types of questions would
have only appeared in science fiction literature. However, an increasing number of scientists (e.g., Carl Sagan) are seriously
considering them as legitimate problems that deserve to be scientifically investigated. In fact, during the last couple of
years several projects have been undertaken to scan incoming radiation from the nearest stars for possible signals that could have
originated from other civilizations. So far, however, the results
have been negative, but further experiments are in preparation and
might bring us one step closer to solving the puzzle of extraterrestrial life.

Problem 10.2: Accident or Necessity:
The Titius-Bode Rule

In 1772 Titius and Bode discovered that the distance of the
planets from the sun follows a simple rule. Using the distance
earth-sun as the unit of measurement, the distances between the
planets and sun are given in good approximation by

$$r_n = 0.4 + 0.3 \times 2^n$$

$$n = -1, 0, 1, 2, \ldots, 8$$

For $n = 3$ there exists no planet but several years after the discovery of the Titius-Bode rule astronomers found the belt of

asteroids at precisely the distance that corresponds to $n = 3$.   Do you consider the Titius-Bode rule a numerical *accident* or a *necessary* law that can be understood through the theory of the evolution of planetary systems?

SOLUTIONS TO SELECTED PROBLEMS

1.1: *Eötvös-Dicke Experiment*

We shall neglect the variation of gravity in the earth's interior in order to simplify the argument (actually, the answer would not change qualitatively). The distance fallen during time t is $x \approx gt^2/2$, while the difference in height Δx of the centers of gravity of the two balls is $\Delta x \approx \Delta g t^2/2$. Consequently,

$$\Delta x/x \approx \Delta g/g \approx 10^{-11}$$

Since $x \approx 10^7$ m, we finally obtain $\Delta x \approx 10^{-4}$ m.

1.2: *Inertial and Gravitational Mass*

The existence of a molecule with distinct inertial and gravitational mass could be incorporated into Newton's theory after minor modifications to the theory. On the other hand, Einstein's theory postulates the identity of inertial and gravitational mass, and a molecule with the above property would be a fatal blow to Einstein's theory. Put differently, the "predictive power" of Einstein's theory is greater than that of Newton's theory.

2.1: *Pound-Snider Experiment*

Generally, $\Delta\nu/\nu = \Delta U/c^2$. For the earth's gravity field we have also $\Delta U = gH$. Thus, for $H = 20$ m we obtain $\Delta\nu/\nu \approx 10 \times 20/10^{17} = 2 \times 10^{-15}$. The success of the experiment rests heavily on the Mössbauer effect, which yields sharply defined spectral lines, allowing accurate red shift measurements.

183

2.2: What Is Straight?

Compare Problem 3.4.

3.1: The Hafele-Keating Experiment

The necessary accuracy of the clocks is $\Delta T/T \approx 1$ nsec/10^5 sec $\approx 10^{-14}$.

3.2: The Twin Paradox

Clearly, we can regard the human body as a clock, even though its precision leaves much to be desired. For example, counting the heart beats could provide a way to measure time. Of course, this time measure is by no means a unique function of the "aging" mentioned in the problem. In addition, the physiological conditions arising during space travel would also influence the aging process to some extent. Therefore, relativistic effects would only become measurable if they significantly exceed the inaccuracy of the human clock, i.e., if they reach or exceed 30%.

3.3: What Is a Plane?

The answer to the question whether our cross section is a plane depends on an analysis of the properties commonly associated with a plane. We can (1) require that the surface "looks plane," in other words, we use light to characterize the surface. Alternatively we could also (2) use tightly stretched ropes in order to verify that the surface is a plane, or (3) we might use measuring sticks to survey the surface, and to see if the geometry is Euclidean (sum of angles in a triangle is 180°, etc.). All three criteria are essentially equivalent in our day-to-day experiences. However, this is not true any longer when we are in the neighborhood of heavy masses.

Thus, in order to answer our initial question whether a surface is a plane or not, we must make up our mind which of the above three criteria are to be applied. For instance, the cross-sectional surface through the center of the sun is a plane only if we use the first criterion.

3.4: Once Again: What Is Straight?

Just as in Problem 3.3 we can define the concept "straight line" in different ways, which are all equivalent in our daily experiences. Any one of these definitions could be used to define "straight" even in a curved space. For instance, we could define the track of a light ray as a straight line. However, in view of our discussion on the deflection of light rays, this definition would not be very useful. In fact, mathematical and physical terminology avoids the use of straight line in connection with curved spaces. Instead, one uses the term "geodesic" for the shortest possible path between two points in a curved space-time. Clearly, this concept is a natural generalization of that of a straight line.

3.5: Life on a Neutron Star

Let us precede the discussion of this and the following problems by noting that due to the enormous gravitational force no known lifeforms could exist on such stars. Also, any buildings would have to consist of hypothetical "supermatter" in order to withstand the crushing forces of gravity.

The shrinking of measuring rods would remain undetected as long as "society" lives only on the surface of the star, building no high-rises or tunnels, and having no airplanes. Should they construct a tunnel, however, leading through the center of the star (which has a diameter of only about 20 km!) then they would discover that this tunnel would be considerably longer than one would have suspected, judging by the circumference of the star.

4.1: Density and Pressure Inside Earth and Sun

A mean solar density of $\rho \approx 1000$ kg/m^3 will, according to Eq. (4.9), yield a pressure in the sun

$$p \approx \rho c^2 \; R/R \approx (10^3 \times 10^{17}) \times 10^{-6} \; N/m^2 = 10^{14} \; N/m^2$$

For earth, $\rho \approx 5000$ kg/m^3, and $R/R \approx 10^{-9}$. Thus

$$p \approx 5 \times 10^{11} \; N/m^2$$

These values for the pressure inside the sun and the earth, resp., compare fairly well with those given in Fig. 4.3.

4.3: Star Formation

Substituting $\rho \approx 10^{-19}$ kg/m^3 and $T \approx 100$ K into the Jeans criterion [Eq. (4.17)] results in the condition $M > 10^4 M_\odot$. This shows that stars cannot form individually but only in association with other stars. As a gas cloud of $10^4 M_\odot$ becomes unstable it starts to slowly contract. As the density rises, smaller masses within the big cloud become unstable [Eq. (4.17)]. The result is a break-up of the initial gas cloud into a number of smaller clouds, which eventually contract to form individual stars. These stars raise the temperature of the remaining gas cloud, thereby ionizing the hydrogen (HII region). The further development of the HII cloud and its embedded stars is discussed in detail in the standard literature on astronomy and astrophysics (compare the bibliography).

4.4: High-Pressure Physics

Equation (4.35) shows that for $\rho = \rho_0$,

$$p_0 = \frac{m}{\mu} \, \rho_0 c^2 \left(\frac{\rho_0}{\rho_c}\right)^{2/3} = \frac{m}{\mu} \, \rho_0 c^2 \alpha^2 \approx 10^{13} \; N/m^2$$

Such high pressures cannot be obtained in laboratory experiments since the atomic structure of the measuring apparatus would be destroyed in the process.

4.5: Planetary Radii

$M \approx \rho_0 R^3$ implies $R_p \approx (M_p/\rho_0)^{1/3} \approx 10^8$ m

The radius of Jupiter is 7×10^7 m.

4.6: The Mass of Main Sequence Stars

For a stable star the radiation pressure must be smaller than the gas pressure; thus

$$p_R \approx \frac{(kT)^4}{(\hbar c)^3} < p = \frac{kT}{\mu} \rho \tag{1}$$

or

$$(kT/\hbar c)^3 < \rho/\mu \tag{2}$$

Using the equilibrium condition

$$kT/\mu c^2 \approx R/R \tag{3}$$

we can eliminate kT from Eq.(2):

$$\left(\frac{kT}{\hbar c}\right)^3 = \left(\frac{R}{R}\frac{\mu c}{\hbar}\right)^3 < \frac{\rho}{\mu} \tag{4}$$

Equation (4) leads to the following inequality for the Schwarzschild radius:

$$R^3 = \frac{G^3 M^3}{c^6} < \frac{(\rho R^3)}{\mu}\frac{\hbar^3}{\mu^3 c^3} = M\frac{\hbar^3}{\mu^4 c^3} \tag{5}$$

and thus

$$M^2 < \frac{\hbar^3 c^3}{\mu^4 G^3} = \bar{\alpha}_G^3 \mu^2 = M_C^2 \tag{6}$$

4.7: Planets and Moons

The electromagnetic binding energy (cohesion energy) of a body consisting of N atoms is $N\varepsilon$, where $\varepsilon \approx 1$ eV. This binding energy is smaller than the cohesion due to gravity if

$$N\varepsilon \lesssim \frac{GM^2}{R} = \frac{GM}{R}(N\mu A) \tag{1}$$

Hence,

$$M/R \approx M^{2/3}\rho^{1/3} > \varepsilon/\mu AG \tag{2}$$

or

$$M > \left(\frac{\varepsilon}{\mu AG}\right)^{3/2} \frac{1}{\rho^{1/2}} \tag{3}$$

Using

$$\rho \approx \rho_p \approx \mu/r_B^3 = \mu\alpha^3(mc/\hbar)^3 \tag{4}$$

we obtain

$$M > \left(\frac{\varepsilon\hbar}{\mu^2 AG\alpha^2 mc}\right)^{3/2} \mu = M_C\alpha^{3/2}\left(\frac{\varepsilon}{A\alpha^2 mc^2}\right)^{3/2}$$

Since $\alpha^2 mc^2 = 27$ eV is twice the binding energy of the lowest energy level of the hydrogen atom, we arrive at the numerical value mentioned in the text.

4.8: Forms and spheres

$$H/R < \varepsilon R/\mu AMG \tag{1}$$

and $M \approx \rho_0 R^3$ yields

$$H/R < \varepsilon/\mu A\rho_0 R^2 G = (R_m/R)^2 \tag{2}$$

Here, $R_m^2 = \epsilon/(\mu A \rho_0 G) \approx (1000 \text{ km})^2$. A more accurate value is $R_m \approx 300$ km.

5.1: Rotation

The given conditions are only valid if the gravitational effects dominate the cohesion energy of the body, since the only attracting force taken into account by Eq.(5.8) is gravity. Problem 4.7 shows that this is the case for $M > 10^{22}$ kg. For white dwarfs $\tau_{rot} > 1$ sec.

6.1: Rotation

In order for a rotating object not to collapse under its own gravitational force we must have

$$v^2 = GM/R \qquad (1)$$

With $M \approx \rho R^3$ and $T_R \approx R/v$, we find

$$T_R = (G\rho)^{-1/2}$$

for the rotation time. Assuming that M is independent of R, we see that the rotational speed $v \propto R^{-1/2}$. An example is the solar system, where we can neglect the masses of the planets; only the sun's mass counts. For objects with an essentially homogeneous density distribution, we have $M = \rho R^3$, $v = G\rho^{1/2} R \propto R$. Both cases are of importance in Problem 6.2.

6.2: Rotation of the Galaxy

The curve in Fig. 6.2 increases almost linearly for $R < 20{,}000$ light years, in agreement with the results of Problem 6.1 for objects of homogeneous density. For larger radii, however, $v^2 \approx GM/R$, i.e. $v \propto R^{-1/2}$. We may conclude that the main mass of our galaxy is confined to a region of $R < 2 \times 10^4$ light years. The mass of the galaxy is given by

$$M \approx Rv^2/G \approx 2 \times 10^{41} \text{ kg} \approx 10^{11} M_{\odot}$$

The rotational velocity of the galaxy (Fig. 6.2) has been determined by making use of the Doppler effect, measuring the frequency
shift of the 21 cm spectral line of hydrogen.

6.3: *Is the Singularity Avoidable?*

After stellar collapse has progressed beyond the Schwarzschild
radius, no force whatsoever will be able to halt it. The reason
for this can be found in Fig. 6.3. Here we see that for $r < R$ the
light cone is tilted inwards, and hence a particle can only fall
inwards, not coming to a stop until $r = 0$, since the lines $r =$
const $< R$ lie outside its local light cone.

6.4: *Density at the Schwarzschild Radius*

Since $R \approx GM/c^2 = R \approx (M/\rho)^{1/3}$, we find that the density of an
object at its Schwarzschild radius is given by

$$\rho = c^6/G^3 M^2 \tag{1}$$

Large masses (e.g., galaxies) will have relatively small densities
at their Schwarzschild radius. To obtain some numerical results,
we rewrite Eq.(1):

$$p = \frac{c^6}{G^3 M_{\odot}^2} \left(\frac{M_{\odot}}{M} \right)^2 \approx 10^{20} \text{ kg/m}^3 \times \left(\frac{M_{\odot}}{M} \right)^2$$

For a galaxy, $M \approx 10^{11} M_{\odot}$; thus $\rho \approx 10^{-2} \text{ kg/m}^3$.

6.6: *Radial Fall*

A particle that is lowered by a rope will reach the point $r =$
R later than a free-falling particle (the rope introduces a delay).
Seen from outside, even a free-falling particle will reach $r = R$
only at $t = \infty$, and hence the particle hanging on a string will
never get beyond $r = R$. The upper limit of energy that can be

gained in this way will therefore be $E_R(R) = -mc^2/2$. This result actually only reflects the correct order of magnitude. One can show that in general it is impossible to extract more energy than the particle's rest energy when lowering it into a gravitational field. Thus, the "perpetuum mobile" mentioned in the text becomes an impossibility.

8.1: Generation of Gravitational Waves

With $\omega \approx 10^3$ sec^{-1}, $m \approx 10$ kg, $r \approx 1$ m, we obtain $P \approx 10^{-33}$ W. Since the rotational energy E_R of such an apparatus is about $E_R \approx 10^7$ W sec, a considerable fraction of the energy is radiated away after

$$T \approx E_R/P = 10^{40} \text{ sec}$$

8.2: Gravitational Waves in the Solar System

The kinetic energy of earth or moon is roughly $E_K = mv^2 \approx mMG/r \approx (mc^2)R_1/r$. The time τ that it takes to radiate 1% of that energy away is given by

$$P\tau = (mc^2)\ \frac{R_1}{r} \times 0.01 \tag{1}$$

Using Eq.(8.11), we obtain

$$\tau \approx 0.01 mc^2 \frac{1}{r} \frac{G}{c^5} \left(\frac{r}{R_1}\right)^3 \left(\frac{r}{R_2}\right) \approx 0.01 \frac{r}{c} \left(\frac{r}{R_2}\right) \left(\frac{r}{R_1}\right)^2 \tag{2}$$

For the system earth-sun this gives $\tau \approx 10^{30}$ sec.

9.1: The Cosmological Principle

Clearly, our main difficulty in verifying the cosmological principle stems from the fact that we only observe the universe from one vantage point, and that we can only get indirect evidence on how the universe looks from other locations. By counting the

galaxies in different directions we are able to gain information
about the isotropy of the universe. This information, however, is
not too accurate. By far the best verification of the isotropy of
the universe has been provided by the cosmic background radiation,
which is discussed in the first section of Chapter 10.

9.2: Extraterrestrial Life

At this point the problem is only meant to stimulate discussion of a topic that is further discussed in Chapter 10.

9.3: Olber's Paradox

No. The integration would only range over a region of several
billion light years, thus giving a finite result.

9.4: Relativity Theory and Speeds Faster Than Light

Special relativity theory prohibits objects or signals from
traveling faster than light within an inertial system. Here the
situation is different since space itself expands, i.e., the local
inertial systems recede from us. Due to the world horizon no
(visible) galaxy will have a measurable speed faster than the
speed of light.

9.5: Newtonian Cosmology

Newton's cosmology is actually a very clever swindle at the
border of mathematical legality. We made the assumption that the
mass distribution outside the sphere shown in Fig. 9.5 does not
contribute to the gravitational force. This argument could be
based on the well-known theorem that a spherical mass distribution
will not create a gravitational field in its interior. What about
infinite mass distributions? In fact, Newton's gravitational potential U of a homogeneous and infinite mass density gives a value
$U = \infty$ at every point. Since the force is given by grad U, one can
avoid the infinity by some clever mathematical manipulations,

reaching a correct result (correct in the sense that it agrees
with general relativity).

9.6: The Early Universe

Right after the start of the expansion, the kinetic energy
dominates everything. Only after kinetic and potential energy are
about equal will the spatial curvature begin to influence the
course of the expansion.

9.7: Models of the Universe

When one regards the surfaces as two-dimensional models of the
universe, one is frequently asked what the significance of the
third dimension in the model is. This leads inevitably to questions about a four-dimensional space, imbedding our warped universe. In order to avoid these problematic considerations we have
preferred to consider the two-dimensional surfaces simply as
mathematical models of cross sections through the universe.

10.1: Duration of the Early Universe

Substituting Eq.(10.7) into Eq.(10.10), we obtain $t_R \approx 10^{12}$
years. Hence, the end of the period of radiation dominance, i.e.,
the duration of the early universe, is about 1 million years.

10.2: Accident or Necessity: The Titius-Bode Rule

Let us quote from a couple of recent works. "Without doubt
the most spectacular property of the solar system is the fact that
the radii of the planetary orbits are not random.... (this sequence) is so regular that any cosmogony which does not explain
this rule must be unacceptable."[1]

[1] Berlage, H. P., "The Origin of the Solar System, p. 5.
Pergamon, Elmsford, New York, 1968.

"The theory must be able to explain the regularities in the planetary motions, their distances from the sun (Bode's rule), and their physical properties."[2]

"We are dealing with an empirical numerical sequence which was discovered by Titius in 1766... and in reality is only a random result."[3]

"The so-called Bode-law is not a physical law but only a convenient rule."[4]

Accident or necessity? Must every planetary system satisfy the Titius-Bode rule? We shall leave it up to the reader to contemplate whether accidental (i.e., random) and necessary properties can be distinguished by inspection of just one object (like our solar system).

[2] *Struve, O., "Astronomie. Einführung in ihre Grundlagen,"* 3rd ed., p. 259. *de Gruyter, Berlin, 1967.*

[3] *Müller, R., "Astronomische Begriffe," p. 60. Bibliographisches Institut, Mannheim, 1964.*

[4] *Whipple, F. L., "Earth, Moon and Planets," p. 93. Harvard Univ. Press, Cambridge, Massachusetts, 1968.*

BIBLIOGRAPHY

1. SPECIAL RELATIVITY

   French, A. P., "Special Relativity." Norton, New York, 1968.
   An excellent text.

   Rindler, W., "Essential Relativity." Van Nostrand Reinhold,
   New York, 1969.
   A clear and didactically excellent introduction into special
   and general relativity theory.

   Taylor, E. F., and Wheeler, J. A., "Spacetime Physics." W. H.
   Freeman, San Francisco, 1966.
   Unorthodox but highly intuitive and entertaining treatment of
   special relativity and curved space-time. Full of illustrations
   and diverse exercises.

2. GENERAL RELATIVITY

   Kaufman, W. III, "Relativity and Cosmology." Harper & Row,
   1973.

   Kaufman, W. III, "The Cosmic Frontiers of General Relativity."
   Little Brown, Boston, 1977.

   Misner, C. W., Thorne, K. S., and Wheeler, J. A., "Gravitation." W. H. Freeman, San Francisco, 1973.
   An outstanding encyclopedic treatment filled with historical
   and philosophical discussions (ca. 1280 pages!).

Weinberg, S., "Gravitation and Cosmology: Principles and Applications of the General Theory of Relativity." Wiley, New York, 1972.

Advanced text containing a detailed analysis of the experiments used to verify relativity.

3. GENERAL ASTRONOMY AND ASTROPHYSICS

Avrett, E. (Ed.), "Frontiers of Astrophysics." Harvard Univ. Press, Cambridge, Massachusetts, 1976.

Contains chapters on neutron stars, black holes and supernovas, and galaxies and cosmology.

Calder, N., "The Key to the Universe: A Report on the New Physics." Viking, New York, 1977.

A popular overview of particle physics and cosmology; based on the TV program.

Calder, N., "Violent Universe." Penguin Books, New York, 1977.

A good popular tour through modern astronomy.

Ginerich, O. (Ed.), "Frontiers of Astronomy: Readings from Scientific American." W. H. Freeman, San Francisco, 1970.

Contains a collection of outstanding articles.

Gribbin, J., "Our Changing Universe: The New Astronomy." Dutton, New York, 1976.

Harwitt, M., "Astrophysical Concepts." Wiley, New York, 1973.

Contains a wide range of topics and extensive bibliography.

Hoyle, F., "Highlights in Astronomy." W. H. Freeman, San Francisco, 1975.

Large selection of excellent color photographs accompany a well-written text.

Swihart, T. L., "Astrophysics and Stellar Astronomy." Wiley, New York, 1968.

Clear and readable introduction to astrophysics.

Unsöld, A., "The New Cosmos," 2nd ed. Springer Verlag, New York, 1977.
A general astronomy text at intermediate to advanced level.

Verschuur, G., "The Invisible Universe: The Story of Radio Astronomy." Springer Verlag, New York, 1974.

4. COSMOLOGY

Asimov, I., "The Collapsing Universe." Walker & Co., New York, 1977.

Bergman, P., "The Riddle of Gravitation." Scribner, New York, 1968.

Berry, M., "Principles of Cosmology and Gravitation." Cambridge Univ. Press, Cambridge, 1976.
Mathematically simple introduction into general relativity, cosmology, and black hole theory.

Ferris, T., "The Red Limit: The Search for the Edge of the Universe." William Morrow, New York, 1977.
Cosmology with many historical and personal anecdotes.

Gribbin, J., "White Holes: Cosmic Gushers in the Universe." Delacorte, New York, 19XX.

Rees, M., Ruffini, R., and Wheeler, J., "Black Holes, Gravitational Waves and Cosmology: An Introduction to Current Research." Gordon & Breach, New York, 1974.
A text for beginning graduate students.

Sciama, D., "Modern Cosmology." Cambridge Univ. Press, Cambridge, 1971.

Shipman, H., "Black Holes, Quasars, and the Universe." Houghton Mifflin, Boston, Massachusetts, 1973.

Wald, R., "Space, Time, and Gravity: The Theory of the Big Bang and Black Holes." Univ. of Chicago Press, Chicago, 1977/

Weinberg, S., "The First Three Minutes, A Modern View of the Origin of the Universe." Basic Books, New York, 1977.

5. EXTRATERRESTRIAL LIFE

Dyson, F. J., The search for extraterrestrial technology, *in* "Perspectives in Modern Physics" (R. E. Marshak, ed.). Krieger, Huntington, New York, 1966.

Macgowan, R. A., and Ordway, F. I., "Intelligence in the Universe," 3rd ed. Prentice-Hall, Englewood Cliffs, New Jersey, 1966.

Sagan, C. (Ed.), "Communication with Extraterrestrial Intelligence." MIT Press, Cambridge, Massachusetts, 19XX.

Sagan, C., and Drake, F., The search for extraterrestrial intelligence, *Scientific American*, 1976.

Sagan, C., and Shklovsky, S., "Intelligent Life in the Universe." Dell, New York, 1968.

INDEX

Phobos, 82
Photon, 10, 167–168
Planck's quantum of action, 10, 67
Plane, 40
Planets, 69–73, 81, 179–180
  radii, 73
  system of, 179–180
Potential, effective, 102
Pound–Snider experiment, 12–13
Pressure, 56
Principle
  cosmological, 142
  Fermat's, 40
  Pauli's, 62
Process, thermodynamic, 178
Pulsar, 84–91
  periods of, 85–86
  physics of, 85

Q

Quadrupol moment, 133–134
Quantum field theory, 1
Quantum mechanics, 1
Quantum of action, Planck's, 10, 67
Quasar, 17

R

Radar signal, 41
Radial fall, 105
Radiation, 167–171
  age of, 173
  black body, 122
  energy, 169
    spectrum, 122
  source of, 138
  thermal, 109–110, 167
Radiation-dominated universe, 169, 171
Radii
  of neutron stars, 77
  of white dwarfs, 68–69
Radio telescope, 84
Radius, Bohr's, 70
Red giants, 61
Redshift, 10–13, 26, 145, 168
  measurements, 12–13
  of spectral lines, 145
Redshift–distance relation, corrections, 160
Reference clock, 31–32
Reference systems, accelerated, 8
Relativity theory,
  general, 1, 9, 102–103
  special, 1

Resonance phenomena, 137
Revolution, Copernican, 141
Ring, semi-transparent, 118
Roche lobe, 120
Rotating black holes, 106–108
Rotational energy, 87

S

Sagan, Carl, 181
Scalar-tensor theory, 9
Schwarzschild radius, 11, 24, 99–101
Science fiction literature, 181
Self-organization of matter, 178
Semi-transparent ring, 118
Shapiro experiment, 19, 41–45
Singularity, 92, 97, 99–101
  naked, 101
Sirius B, 69
Solar system, 179
Solar wind, 180
Sommerfeld's fine structure constant, 67
Space
  curved, 38, 45, 155
  Euclidean, 158
  hyperbolic, 158, 160, 162
  Minkowski, 38
  Riemannian, 2, 38
  spherical, 158–160
  structure of, 38
Space-time
  curvature of, 38, 45
  geometry, 40–41
  oscillations of, 132
Spaces of constant curvature, 156–158
Spaceship, 4–5
Spectral lines, redshift of, 145
Spectrum, of degenerate stars, 76
Speed
  faster than light, 150
  of light, effective, 42
  of sound, 89
Spheres, 81
Stability condition, 52–56
Star, frozen, 101
Stars, 52–83
  age of, 173
  degenerate, 61–69, 73–78
  nondegenerate, 59–61
  normal, 60–61
  variable, 90
Stefan–Boltzmann law, 169
Stellar
  clusters, 177

RETURN PHYSICS LIBRARY
TO ➡ 351 LeConte Hall   642-3122

LOAN PERIOD 1	2	3
1-MONTH		
4	5	6

ALL BOOKS MAY BE RECALLED AFTER 7 DAYS
Overdue books are subject to replacement bills

DUE AS STAMPED BELOW

APR 1 3 1994		
Rec'd UCB PHYS		
DEC 2 1 1994		
DEC 1 2 1994		
Rec'd UCB PHYS		
SEP 1 1 1999		
NOV 0 9 2003 DEC 1 9 2005		
NOV 1 8 2006 NOV 0 2 2007		

FORM NO. DD 25

UNIVERSITY OF CALIFORNIA, BERKELEY
BERKELEY, CA 94720

Ⓟs